# BERMUDA
# TEN COASTAL WALKS

St. George'

Dockyard

Hamilton

## COASTAL WALKS
1. Nonsuch Island
2. Whalebone Bay & Railway Trail
3. Warwick Long Bay Nature Reserve & South Shore Park
4. Spittal Pond Nature Reserve
5. Cooper's Island Nature Reserve and Clearwater Beach
6. Blue Hole Nature Reserve
7. Alfred Blackburn Smith Nature Reserve
8. Bermuda Botanical Gardens
9. Fort Scaur and the Railway Trail
10. North Shore Railway Trail

All photographs were taken by the author unless otherwise noted.

Book design by Amy K. Pearson and Alfred J. Pearson

BOOK ORDERS: Through publisher or telephone: 508-847-9910

BioQuill Publishing
PO Box 157
Princeton, MA 01541
USA
www.BioQuill.com

Title:  Coastal Bermuda 10 Walks and 73 Plants...you'll see along the way

ISBN 978-0-615-20530-4

Front cover is Spittal Pond Nature Reserve
Back cover is the Author at South Shore Park taken by Alfred J. Pearson

# COASTAL BERMUDA
## 10 Walks and 73 Plants...
## you'll see along the way

Amy K. Pearson

BERMUDA FACTS
Latitude: 32°20' N
Longitude: 64°40' W
Avg. Air Temp: 22°C/72°F
Avg. Water Temp: 23°C/73.5°F
Island Length: ≈35 km/21 mi
Island Area: ≈50 km²/21 mi²
Highest Elevation: 79 m/259 ft.
Population: 68,500

# TABLE OF CONTENTS                                        PAGE NUMBER

## THE COASTAL PLANTS

Order based on proximity to ocean, with #1-34 among the closest, # 35-41 are grasses at variable distance from the water, # 42-54 fairly close to ocean/salt water, and #55-73 are found in more upland or inland coastal areas.

# PREFACE

I have had the privilege of visiting Bermuda at least once a year for the last ten years. First as a student learning about this unique oceanic island, then as a teacher bringing high school students to the island for a seven-day intensive course in Marine and Island Ecology. I was repeatedly awestruck by the rich diversity of plants, especially the coastal species with their unique survival adaptations. I thought them beautiful and wanted to learn more about them.

I could not find a book that identfied and gave information about all of the coastal plants. Nathaniel Lord Britton's out of print book , *Flora of Bermuda* (1918) was the most comprehensive source I could find.[5] I felt a book focused on just the coastal plants would be of interest and a help to others. With that inspiration, my goal was to keep it simple and provide a useful resource guide for anyone who enjoys coastal and beach exploration. This book utilizes a field guide approach with color photos and user friendly descriptions in a format that can easily be taken along on hikes.

The meeting of ocean and land creates a unique environment rich in things to explore. Of those, the coastal plants present a fair share, offering a balanced green contrast to the oceanic turquoise. As we take the time to appreciate and learn more about the plants of the coast, the role they play in their environment will become more apparent. Hopefully, along the way more attention and consideration will be drawn to maintenance and preservation of these beautiful native plants and habitats. Preserving the coastlines of Bermuda is of universal value to both Bermudian residents and visitors alike.

From a practical standpoint, many of the native plants act to hold down coastlines during storms and hurricanes. The native and endemic coastal plants are quite beautiful and a centrally important part of the natural scene that should be preserved. Their presence contributes to the plant diversity not only on this small island but globally as well. A rich biological diversity creates a stable ecological system that provides for interactions between many different types of living things. A challenge to these plants is coastal development. Pressure to build on and/or change the plant habitats on coastal property is continuous. Alternatively, landscaping that incorporates maintenance and preservation of the native and endemic plants can create great beauty and provide a living history unique to this Island.

It is my hope that the reader enjoys the plant photos, information, and walks presented. Connecting with the world through these coastal walks and plant discoveries should bring you inner joy, wonder ... and a desire to return.

# ACKNOWLEDGMENTS

One cannot create a document like this without the help of many. The range of support I received was huge. I first thank my husband Alfred, for his support and advice throughout this project. His wisdom, direction, organizational and editing skills helped make this happen.

Because I do not live in Bermuda, I needed support from Island residents in the preparation of this book. David Wingate has been inspirational in his creation of Nonsuch Island as a living museum of Bermuda's native and endemic plants. His help in locating rare plants, identification of others, and recommendations of what should be included was essential for the completion of this book. His intimate knowledge of every plant and its ecological relationships was shared and much appreciated.

Helge Wingate offered help in locating certain plants on the Island as well, and our hunt for some of the photographs in this book made the process even more enjoyable. Her knowledge of the plants, some found in her own yard, was immensely helpful.

Fiona Doe, an arborist and owner of Bermuda's Tree Care & Training, has been a wonderful resource, identifying or confirming photos through internet correspondence.

Jane Burrows at BIOS (Bermuda Institute for Ocean Sciences) has been helpful in many ways, from finding me a place to sleep to supplying me with general information about Bermuda. Lauren Yelle-Simons at BIOS has also been very supportive throughout this process.

Lisa Greene at the Bermuda Aquarium, Natural History Museum and Zoo was helpful in plant identification and I have learned much from her articles in the *Mid-Ocean News*. Bermuda is fortunate to have her.

Bancroft School located in Worcester, Massachusetts, where I have taught science for thirty years, has offered me many opportunities for professional development including a Fargo-Gauthier Grant to study in Bermuda back in 1997. This book could not have been created without a sabbatical leave, granted by the school for the fall of 2007. I thank Rhonda Poire and Bud Brooks of the technology department at Bancroft School for their technical support. In preparing the layout of the book, Connie Moore of Bancroft School's art department and Dan Smith of Herff Jones Yearbooks, provided essential assistance in design and software application for book layout. Their willingness to share information, make suggestions and answer questions was greatly appreciated.

I also want to thank the many friends and family I solicited for opinions on book size, layout and design. I'm indebted for the help I've received from so many. I had no idea how much is involved in writing, designing, laying out, and publishing a book.

# INTRODUCTION

Whether this is your first visit to Bermuda or you live on the Island, this book is intended to enrich your experience on the Island. It can be used as a reference when exploring any beach or coastal area. It is easy to take with you for on-site identification. As a visitor to Bermuda (or even a resident!) exploration time may be limited, so I've included ten coastal walks that will introduce you to beautiful vistas, plants and surroundings.

The plants described herein (each on a single page) are the 73 species I consider to be primarily coastal, that is their natural habitat is relatively near the water's edge. Each plant page is headed by the plant's common or local name with the scientific name (genus, species) and botanical family name to the right. Below the common name I give an indication as to the plant's origin/status (native, endemic, or naturalized) followed by a descriptive term such as tree, shrub or vine. To aid in locating an example of the plant, a list of locations is also provided.

Most people prefer common or local names when describing and learning about a plant. I have emphasized these names as these are most frequently used in conversation. Scientific names (genus and species) are names given to all organisms to minimize

ambiguous identification. They are essential in proper plant identification as there are sometimes two or more plants that look very much alike. These names insure correct identification based upon specific traits of the plant. In the system of naming plants, all plants have been classified into a catagory called Family whose name usually ends in "eae". These botanical families include plants with similar characteristics, such as number of flower petals, type of leaf, and so on.

Plant measurements given in this book are an average for the plant. There may exist a plant whose size falls outside the value given. Do consider this when identifying a plant. The locations indicated where each plant can be found are places I have seen them or have reliable evidence of their existence. Plants may be in other locations that I have not recorded and they may be absent from the location where I observed them. Nature is in control of this!

When describing the plants, I have tried to use terms that all people will understand. Botanical terminology is kept to a minimum and has been translated into more common language. For example, I have used cluster to describe a stem with many small flowers, rather than the botanical term of inflorescence. Where botanical terms are used, they are defined in the glossary and often parenthetically within the description. Botanical terms were created to uniquely and specifically

describe certain plant features, however I did not want new language to get in the way of the reader's experience. I hope that botanists using this book will not be too dismayed and that all others will benefit from the simplicity of the language. Hopefully you will learn a bit of both as you use this book!

Information presented about some of the plants as being edible or having been used to produce drinks are based on research or anecdotes. They have not been tested by me nor are they my recommended uses for the plants.

I took the majority of the photographs with a ten megapixel, Canon Power Shot A640 camera. This compact camera was easy to use, even for a novice photographer and compact for efficiency in the field. No alteration of plant structure was done for any of the photos.

# BERMUDA the ISLAND

Today Bermuda's pink beaches, rocky shores, turquoise water and dramatic vistas attract many visitors. It boasts the world's northernmost coral reefs as well as the Atlantic Ocean's northernmost mangrove swamps. It is a short plane ride from the east coast of the USA and Canada making it an enticing travel destination. When exploring the Island, you will find wherever you look there is something strikingly beautiful. Preservation of its open spaces and natural habitats is more important than ever before as the demand for development increases.

Bermuda appeared on earth in a rather exciting way. Somewhere between 100 and 115 million years ago near the mid-Atlantic ridge, an underwater volcano erupted producing several seamounts, one of which would eventually become the Island of Bermuda. As the crustal plate that this original seamount sat on moved westward, a second eruption occurred about 35 million years ago. The second eruption rose from an ocean depth of about 4 km (2.4 miles) and although the growing seamount was covered by water, a rich coral reef ecosystem developed around it. When the ice ages occurred (over 60 glacial advances/retreats have occurred in just the last 2 million years[40]) they produced a drop in sea level. This resulted in Bermuda becoming a good-sized island complete with a coral reef ecosystem. Over the years as the Island eroded, the calcium bearing coral and other reef organisms were broken down to generate the sands of Bermuda. This is described as biogenic sand and is unlike silica-based sand. To demonstrate this, touch some dry sand with a wet hand or foot. It's very sticky, unlike silica-based sand found in other parts of the world. The other noteworthy quality of this

sand are the pink specks in it. Looking closely at the sand, the color is due to polished pieces of pink, shell-like material. This shell was produced by a marine creature that one rarely sees, a foraminiferan or foram called *Homotrema rubrum*. Forams are one-celled protists that live on the bottom, attaching themselves to other shells and reef material. Their shell has tiny holes through which minute tentacles extend to capture food.

They bring people joy by inadvertently creating pink sand.

The sands formed dunes (you can see some today!). As water percolated through the sand, it cemented some together forming the limestone rock found in Bermuda today. When you see it along the coastal walks, it appears grayish, almost like granite or some types of lava rock…do not be deceived! It is limestone that has cyanobacteria (tiny algae) living on it, causing the black and dark gray colors.

*Sargassum* (a brown seaweed) that commonly washes up on Bermuda's pink beaches

Over time, Bermuda evolved into five main islands (presently connected by bridges) and approximately 175 small islands.

It is not a tropical island but rather sub-tropical, kept warm by the Gulf Stream that travels between the United States and Bermuda. The closest mainland is Cape Hatteras, North Carolina, which is about 1083 km (650 miles) west of Bermuda. Bermuda's latitude is the same as North Carolina, however Bermuda has a warmer climate. Making it even more special is the fact that it is quite small, only 35 km (about 21 miles) long and from 1-3 km wide making its area just 50 km$^2$ ( 21 square miles).

Due to its isolation and dangerous reefs, Bermuda was not settled until the British ship Sea Venture was shipwrecked here in 1609 as it was heading for Jamestown in Virginia. There were no native mammals on the island and it was forested with the endemic Bermuda cedar (*Juniperus bermudiana*). Today, with a population of 68,500, Bermuda is a British overseas territory with its own government. The Queen appoints a governor who acts as liaison between the UK and Bermuda and is also responsible for external affairs and defense of the territory.

Bermuda's botanical history has been an eventful one. The plants that resided on Bermuda before man arrived got there via wind, water, rafting on some piece of floating material or were transported by birds in their feathers or digestive systems. Human interaction affected plant life as ways were found to use the plants for shelter, food and even transportation. The endemic Bermuda cedar made fine ship building material! Conservation measures by the British came not long after settlement as there was soon a shortage of the cedar. In 1622 the government instituted some of the first conservation laws for the new world, limiting the cutting of cedars.[17] This kept the Island naturally forested until the unintentional introduction of several damaging cedar scale insects traveling on nursery plants in the early 20th century. By 1955, 90% of the endemic cedar had been destroyed. A few cedar survivors able to resist the scale insect were cultivated for planting. While this was happening, another plant, the Australian whistling pine or *Casuarina* (*Casuarina equisetifolia*) was planted to replace the endemic cedars and act as a windbreak along coastlines. It quickly became an invasive species as it was fast growing and did not allow the natural understory (or anything!) to grow beneath it. In high winds and hurricanes it toppled (unlike the cedar) spreading its seeds and breaking apart the limestone rock that held its roots. Today, through conservation efforts, the scale resistant cedar is making a comeback though invasives still fiercely compete for the limited space.

**Native** plants are those that arrived by natural means and were able to establish themselves. By natural it is meant that seed or plant material arrived via wind, water, rafting or transportation by birds, fish, or animal.

Examples of native species include most of the grasses, iodine bush, beach lobelia, sea lavender, and more. **Endemic** plants are those that are only found in a small geographic area and most likely evolved in isolation as unique species through differentiation from native species. The plants in this book considered **endemic to Bermuda** include Bermuda cedar, Bermudiana, Bermuda olivewood, Bermuda palmetto, Bermuda snowberry, Bermuda bean and Darrell's fleabane. **Naturalized** plants are those that were brought to Bermuda by man and were able to establish themselves within the environment. Some of these plants are Natal plum, oleander, hibiscus and Surinam cherry. A subset of naturalized species are **invasive** species. These are plants that can out-compete native or endemic species for space. Invasives usually produce many viable seeds and have physical qualities that hinder growth of natives. When invasives take over a native's niche, it often affects other species by removing a nesting site, food source, or even a hurricane-resistant windbreak that had been provided by a native. The coastal plants described in this book represent all three groups, however a large proportion of them are native.

# COASTAL PLANTS

Plants of the coastal regions have unique adaptations that allow them to survive and thrive in the demanding oceanside environment. The coastal regions of Bermuda show a greater number of native plants than any other Bermuda habitat. This is because of the challenges the coastal environment presents. These plants either first took hold here because of their natural ability to do so or evolved adaptations that provided the ability where none had existed. Sandy terrain drains water easily so beach and shore plants need specialized mechanisms to retain water. Salt in the water and blown in air spray has the effect of drawing out water and causing dehydration. Plants in the coastal regions must contend with this. Due to the challenging environment and the preponderance of open water, rock and sand, relatively few plants can survive here. There is often little shade protection from the sun and absence of protection from the wind. This means that plants of the coast are required to deal with rapid evaporation and the physical disturbances of the wind.

## PLANT ADAPTATIONS TO MAINTAIN HYDRATION

Many coastal plants have fleshy leaves that enable them to store water. Succulents are plants with leaves (and sometimes stems) that store water. Look for this in prickly pear cactus (*Opuntia stricta*) and woody glasswort (*Salicornia perennis*). Other adaptations that provide success in dry, salty environments are leaves with an outer layer (cuticle) covered with a waxy chemical that slows evaporation. This can be seen in Natal plum (*Carissa grandiflora*) and sea purslane (*Sesuvium portulacastrum*). Some plants depend on their small leaf surface area to reduce exposure to air. Grasses such as salt grass (*Spartina patens*) curl their leaf blades during the day to reduce leaf surface area. Plants such as coast spurge (*Chamaesyce mesembrianthemifolia*) curl their leaves close to the stem to prevent water loss. Other plants such as fennel have small leaves or reduced, scale-like leaves such as in Bermuda cedar (*Juniperus bermudiana*) which helps to decrease water loss. Another water saving feature is the tiny surface hair found on leaves and/or stems. These hairs act to block the openings (stomata) in the leaf surface from releasing too much water. This is seen in beach croton (*Croton punctatus*) and common sage bush (*Lantana involucrata*) leaves. Another structural feature observed on some plants is the arrangement of the leaves on the stem. Keeping leaves compact and close to the stem prevents dehydration. This can be seen in the tassel plant (*Suriana maritime*) or coast spurge (*Chamaesyce mesembrianthemifolia*). Most grasses have underground stems called rhizomes that enable them to spread rapidly and reestablish themselves if part of the plant is washed away. This also protects the stem from drying out and promotes more structural stability for the plant. Some invasives like seaside daisy (*Wedelia trilobata*) also spread in this fashion and are quite successful on coastal dunes. Finally, some plants have built-in salt glands that excrete excess salt, including sea lavender (*Limonium carolinianum*), red and black mangroves, and salt grass (*Spartina patens*).

# NONSUCH ISLAND

**Plants to look for:**
forestiera, Bermuda cedar, sea ox-eye, lantana, beach lobelia, southern hackberry, white stopper, Bermuda snowberry, Darrell's fleabane, grey nickers, box briar, small passion flower, salt grass, *Casuarina*, seven-year apple, Bermuda palmetto, buttonwood, Bermuda olivewood, seaside morning glory, Key West gentian, wild stock, seashore rush grass and more!

Nonsuch is a 15-acre island near the entrance to Castle Harbor. It is government property and has been designated a Nature Reserve of the Bermuda Government Parks Dept. The name Nonsuch means "none other" and this island is truly a very special place. In 1962, the Living Museum project for this Nature Reserve was initiated. This occurred shortly after the destruction of Bermuda's endemic juniper (cedar) forest by an accidentally introduced insect pest, which had left all of the trees on Nonsuch dead. These had been replaced by *Lantana* (sage bush) scrub and St. Augustine grass cover. The Living Museum project was conceived and developed by Bermudian naturalist and former chief Conservation Officer, David Wingate. Its goal was, and is, to ecologically restore a small part of Bermuda to pre-colonial conditions. The island is so topographically diverse that it supports representative samples of virtually every habitat found on mainland Bermuda. All of the native and endemic plants described in this book are found on Nonsuch in their native settings. Because of the sensitive nature of this project, public access to the island is limited. Any contact with mainland Bermuda could bring in species not meant to be there, pollution, and invasives. Today Nonsuch Island has been transformed and is a fine example of what someone with a vision and much hard work, can accomplish. In addition, the endemic Bermuda Cahow (a sea bird that breeds only on the outer islands of Bermuda) is being re-established on Nonsuch Island.

*Directions: Limited access. Contact Conservation Services at 441-293-2727*

# WHALEBONE BAY and RAILWAY TRAIL

**Railway trail length - approximately 1 km (0.6 mi.) one-way**

**Plants to look for:**
Bermuda cedar, *Casuarina*, Natal plum, sea ox-eye, Bermuda palmetto, Chinese fan palm, Brazil pepper, fennel, Spanish bayonet, seaside morning glory, sea purslane, wild poinsettia, bay grape, buttonwood, asparagus fern, prickly pear, sheathed paspalum, switch grass, St. Augustine grass, seaside daisy, cape weed, red mangrove, black mangrove, Surinam cherry, jumbie bean, turnera

The Railway Trail here provides amazing ocean views and solitude. This location combines a walk along rocky cliffs with a walk along a shallow bay. Martello Tower and Powder Magazine are located at the western end of the trail, closer to Whalebone Bay. Length of the trail is about 1 km from end to end but can be shortened at any point. It can be lengthened by taking some of the side trails off the main Railway Trail that lead into Ferry Point Park. These are well-traveled paths that are easy to see. Whalebone Bay has a small sandy beach where you'll see buttonwood, bay grape, scurvy grass, sea ox-eye and many other plants. The beach area is larger at low tide, and decreases significantly at high tide. The rest of the bay is lined with rocks. Snorkeling is great here, especially if you follow the rocks encircling the bay. It is possible to see fish in the water as you walk along the sides of the bay. If you follow the Railway Trail to the right (to the east), it will take you along a rocky shoreline. Steep cliffs abound! Look down for grazing turtles and graceful longtails. Look to the right for lush vegetation including Natal plum, Spanish bayonet, prickly pear, sea ox-eye and more. If you walk about 0.5 km from Whalebone Bay, you will see Lover's Lake off to the right. There are paths that can take you to the lake to explore the mangroves.

*Directions:* *The best way to access this area is to travel (by taxi, scooter, or private vehicle) to the end of Ferry Rd. (off of Mullet Bay Rd.). There is a turnaround here, and one can park on the side of the road. To use the public bus system, ask the bus driver to drop you off at Ferry Rd. (for the energetic individual). Then walk about 1 km to a sign (on your right) for the Railway Trail. Follow this cut through (a bit rough) to the Trail, which will be to your left at the end. Alternatively, walk 2 km to Whalebone Bay along Ferry Rd. (it will be on your right) and begin here. There are no sidewalks here, so be careful. The walk is lovely and you will observe high diversity of plant life along the road. Keep your eyes open for the rare turnera on the right!*

15

# WARWICK LONG BAY and SOUTH SHORE PARK

**Trail length - 1.2 km (1 mi.) one way**

The South Shore Park is a uniquely beautiful place. Its beaches are among the most beautiful on the Island. It is located on the western end of the South Shore. Most of the plants that thrive on sandy beaches and dunes described in this book reside here. The trails above the beaches take you through dense vegetation and provide outstanding views. If you hike along Warwick Long Bay, the distance is about 0.5 km (0.2 mi.). You can hike from Warwick Long Bay all the way to Horseshoe Bay. This distance is approximately 1.5 km (about 1 mi.). This trail gives you options to go down to a pink beach or to stay above it. Plant types will vary as the habitat varies, which makes this a spectacular plant viewing hike. When on the beach, some of the plants you will see are seashore rush grass spreading along the beach, coastal spurge, beach lobelia, iodine plant and seaside morning glory. There are large stands of certain plants, creating a naturally beautiful drama.

**Plants to look for:** Bermuda cedar, *Casuarina*, sea ox-eye, Bermuda palmetto, Chinese fan palm, Brazil pepper, fennel, Spanish bayonet, seaside morning glory, sea purslane, wild poinsettia, bay grape, buttonwood, asparagus fern, sheathed paspalum, switch grass, St. Augustine grass, cape weed, Surinam cherry, jumbie bean, scurvy grass, coast spurge, Blodgett's spurge, bay bean, iodine bush or bay lavender, tassel plant, beach croton, seaside goldenrod, oleander, common sage bush, Bermudiana, seashore rush grass, salt grass, West Indian grass, southern burr grass, seaside daisy, yellow Bermuda bean, Japanese pittosporum, beach evening primrose, tamarisk, Jamaica vervain, coast sophora, wild stock

***Directions:*** *To get to the park take the South Shore road to a sign identifying Warwick Long Bay Park. Ample parking is available. Public buses (#7) are also an option, as they travel along the South Shore Road. You could also begin this hike at Horseshoe Bay and head east, ending at Warwick Long Bay.*

# SPITTAL POND NATURE RESERVE

Trail length - 1.8 km loop (1.1 mi.)

Spittal Pond is a coastal Bermuda treasure even though it does not contain a sandy pink beach. Located on the South Shore, toward the eastern end, it is mainland Bermuda's largest nature reserve. The path makes a loop from the parking area, traveling along the rocky coast, then around Spittal Pond and back. The entire loop is approximately 1.8 km (or 1.1 mi.). Heading to your right (counterclockwise) takes you to the pond first, while heading left will take you to the rocky shore. This loop gives a diverse view of different habitats, from rocky shoreline with breath-taking views (complete with splashing surf hitting rocks) to a brackish pond. The pond attracts birds, a fine place to view them. You will see many different plants in one delightful walk. Other highlights found here include Spanish Rock, a rock bearing markings believed to date back to 1543 and Jeffrey's Hole, a cave overlooking the ocean, with access though a cliff-top hole. A story reveals that this cave was a refuge for an escaped slave.

**Plants to look for:** Bermuda cedar, *Casuarina*, Bermuda olivewood, Natal plum, sea ox-eye, Bermuda palmetto, Chinese fan palm, Brazil pepper, fennel, Spanish bayonet, seaside morning glory, sea purslane, wild poinsettia, bay grape, buttonwood, asparagus fern, prickly pear, sheathed paspalum, switch grass, St. Augustine grass, cape weed, seaside daisy, red mangrove, black mangrove, Surinam cherry, jumbie bean, Bermudiana, seaside goldenrod, coast sophora, tassel plant

*Directions: Excellent parking and public bus access are both available. The bus that travels the South Shore Rd. (#1) will drop you at Spittal Pond, just ask the driver.*

# COOPER'S ISLAND NATURE RESERVE and CLEARWATER BEACH

**Trail length - 1.6 km (1.2 mi.) for both trails**

At the eastern end of Bermuda, on the island known as Cooper's Island, one finds some wonderful coastal walks. Cooper's Island was once a separate island however when the airfield was built in the 1940's, Cooper's Island was enlarged (Clearwater Beach was built after 1941 from material remaining from airport construction) and connected to St. David's Island. Clearwater Beach is a short beach walk of about 0.3 km. It is a low energy beach, with gentle surf unlike the more energetic South Shore beaches. Just beyond a small headland on the right of Clearwater Beach is a smaller, more private beach called Turtle Bay. Here you will find many sandy shore plants seen in this book. A large stand of beach croton is here, as well as seaside morning glory, and seashore rush grass. Across the street from Clearwater Beach is Cooper's Island Nature Reserve. There is a part of the Railway Trail here, which takes visitors along the top of steep, coastal hillsides and provides for amazing views of Castle Harbor and Nonsuch Island. The trail makes a loop and is approximately 1 km long. One can take some side trails that increase the distance a bit.

**Plants to look for:** Bermuda cedar, *Casuarina*, sea ox-eye, Bermuda palmetto, Chinese fan palm, Brazil pepper, fennel, Spanish bayonet, seaside morning glory, sea purslane, wild poinsettia, bay grape, buttonwood, asparagus fern, sheathed paspalum, switch grass, St. Augustine grass, cape weed, jumbie bean, scurvy grass, coast spurge, Blodgett's spurge, bay bean, iodine bush or bay lavender, tassel plant, beach croton, seaside evening primrose, seaside goldenrod, oleander, Bermudiana, seashore rush grass, salt grass, West Indian grass, seaside daisy, yellow Bermuda bean, Japanese pittosporum, tamarisk, Jamaica vervain, Jamaica dogwood, fiddlewood, white stopper, Key West gentian, Bermuda olivewood

*Directions: There is no bus service to Cooper's Island, however taxi or scooters can access it. There is a parking area and Clearwater Beach has a concession stand and lifeguard.*

# BLUE HOLE NATURE RESERVE

**Trail length - 0.3-0.8 km (0.25-0.5 mi.) one way**

## Plants to look for:

Bermuda cedar, *Casuarina*, Natal plum, sea ox-eye, Bermuda palmetto, Chinese fan palm, Brazil pepper, fennel, Spanish bayonet, wild poinsettia, bay grape, buttonwood, asparagus fern, sheathed paspalum, cape weed, Surinam cherry, jumbie bean, oleander, Bermudiana, St. Augustine grass, forestiera, allspice, white stopper, Bermuda olivewood, small passion flower, Bermuda bean, seaside heliotrope, woody glasswort, Bermuda snowberry, southern hackberry

Blue Hole Park lies along Castle Harbor, thus its coastal area is a low energy shoreline, due to being in a protected harbor. Blue Hole is a great place to see mangroves as well as other native and endemic trees. Some trees are identified with markers. From the car park, follow the path that starts as a small dirt road and narrows to a trail. Take side trips to your left to explore the mangroves near the water. This trail takes you to a lovely little lagoon surrounded by mangroves and containing one of the many underwater caves found in this area. Its opening is clearly seen from a viewing platform. This walk is approximately 0.3 km (0.25 mi.). There is a path from Blue Hole into Walsingham Reserve that is an additional 0.5 km (0.3 mi.) to the Idwal Hughes Nature Reserve. It starts just before you reach the viewing platform, off to the right. It can be a bit confusing as there are paths off this main path. If you stay on the main path, it leads to Walsingham Lake, then to the Idwal Hughes Nature Reserve. This area has some of the oldest trees on the island, including a large Bermuda cedar, forestiera, the endangered Bermuda bean, and many others. You may "exit here" and follow the driveway from Tom Moore's Tavern to Harrington Sound Rd. where you can catch a bus.

*Directions:* To reach Blue Hole Reserve, if heading to the airport (east) from the west (Hamilton), Blue Hole Park is on the right side shortly after passing the Grotto Bay Beach Resort. Public buses (#1,3,10, & 11) stop at Grotto Bay Beach Resort; one can get off here and take the short walk down the hill to the park. There is also a parking area for scooters. Bus # 1 or 3 travel on Harrington Sound Rd. where Tom Moore's Tavern is located.

# ALFRED BLACKBURN SMITH NATURE RESERVE

**Trail Length - Coastal ridgeline trail is approximately 0.5 km (0.3 mi.) one way**

**Plants to look for:** allspice, fiddlewood, Bermuda snowberry, Darrell's fleabane, Bermuda cedar, Jamaica vervain, box briar, Bermudiana, turnera, buttonwood, sea ox-eye, coast spurge, beach lobelia, bay lavender, Bermuda olivewood, yellow wood, coast sophora, West Indian grass, seashore rush grass, southern hackberry and more!

This approximately 8-acre reserve is a unique spot in Bermuda, as it contains a small section of South Shore coastline (the cliff-top trail rising some 30 m above the water) that holds some of the rarest native plants of Bermuda. For the past ten years the reserve has been attended by environmentalist and horticultural trainees, with continued management by the Audubon Society. Invasives have been culled and native and endemics have been planted. Upon entering from the South Rd., one can follow a steep slope through a forest of naturalized allspice, fiddlewood, Chinese fan palm, and *Casuarinas*. Look closely for Bermuda snowberry and Darrell's fleabane. Those entering from the Coral Beach Club take the ridge top trail that provides a view of the more open coastal slope. Diversity of plant life is greater here as there is less shade. Look for Bermuda cedar, Jamaica dogwood, Japanese pittosporum, and the rare box briar. Other plants mixed in are turnera, Darrell's fleabane, Jamaica vervain, and Bermudiana. At the southwestern end of the reserve, the ridge top trail enters a rocky coastal zone that offers good views of coast spurge, sea ox-eye, tassel plant, buttonwood and several native grasses.

*Directions:* The Reserve is located on South Rd., just west of the Coral Beach Club entrance. There is a sign marking the entrance of the reserve on the South Rd. One can travel there by the South Shore Bus (#7) and ask to get off at the Coral Beach Club (a convenient landmark). If you drive there, you can enter the Coral Beach Club driveway, make the first paved right, follow the uppermost drive to a hairpin turn. Walk over the grass to a natural path directly off the end of the hairpin turn. Continue on foot onto the ridge top to the right, where you will meet the nature trail.
Access limited to members of the Bermuda Audubon Society or by appointment through the Audubon Society; Guests and members of the adjacent Coral Beach Club also have visiting privileges. Bermuda Audubon Society phone: 292-1920; www.audubon.bm or info@audubon.bm

# BERMUDA BOTANICAL GARDENS

Trail Length - "Flat Path" - 185 m (600 ft); Numerous other paths of different lengths;
Entire garden area is 36 acres

If time in Bermuda is limited and you want to see some of the plants in this book, though not necessarily in their native habitat, the Bermuda Botanical Gardens is the place to visit. Here you will find a fine collection of native plants as well as many exotics and other plants that are cultivated or grown in Bermuda. There are over 35 different areas devoted to special plants, such as daylillies, ficus trees, and native and endemic plants, as well as a woodlands walk, rock garden, kitchen gardens, rose garden, butterfly garden, sensory garden, hibiscus, palms, formal gardens and subtropical fruit garden. The grounds are extremely well cared for and a delight to the senses. Camden House, the official residence of the Premier is on the grounds as well. It is used for some official functions and is open for very limited hours. There is also a snack bar and book/gift shop to visit.

**Directions:** *Berry Hill Rd., Point Finger Rd. and South Rd.;  phone: 236-5291  Free admission*
*There are two entrances, Berry Hill Rd. and Point Finger Rd., Paget Parish.  The visitor center is open M-F,  9:30-3:30.  Free tours are given at 10:30am on Tuesday, Wednesday and Friday. Taxi, or private vehicles  (parking is available) can be used to reach this spot, as well as Bus # 1, 2 or 7.*

# FORT SCAUR & the RAILWAY TRAIL

Trail length - approximately 2 km (1.3 mi.) one way

**Plants to look for:** jumbie bean, Brazil pepper, Surinam cherry, fennel, a huge ficus tree, asparagus fern, many exotics, diverse grasses
**At the fort look for:** large Bermuda cedars, turnera under cultivation, endemic maidenhair fern inside the entrance to a storage area for gunpowder

This trail is easy to get to if you are staying on the west end of the island or at the Dockyard. It is scooter-friendly, and one can enjoy a scooter ride without any other type of vehicle on the Railway Trail. The plants on this trail are mainly introduced and naturalized plants, very few natives or endemics. There is a wooden walking bridge over a part of the trail adjacent to a huge ficus tree which offers a feast for the eyes. From the trail there are signs pointing uphill to the fort. There is also a path along the fort's moat, however it does not take visitors up to the fort (it does however offer an interesting walk). This 19th-century fort was built to protect the Dockyard and it offers outstanding views of the Sound. It is very well-maintained (including the rest rooms) and has excellent signs explaining different aspects of the fort.

*Directions: Travel northwest on Middle Rd., crossing the Somerset Bridge. Middle Rd. becomes Somerset Rd. here. Take the second right after the bridge which will take you to a paved section of the railway trail on your left. It is for walking and only cycles (scooters!). Bus #7 or 8 travels on Middle Rd. to Somerset Rd. and you can get off here or begin at Fort Scaur. Coming from the Dockyard you can get off at Somerset Bridge and walk back or get off at Fort Scaur, explore there and then follow the signs to the railway trail.*

# NORTH SHORE RAILWAY TRAIL

Trail length - approximately 0.7 km (0.4 mi.) one way

**Plants to look for:** buttonwood, tamarisk, chicory, *Casuarina*, bay grape, different grasses, Chinese fan palm, sea ox-eye, seaside goldenrod

This trail is a splendid section of the North Shore Railway Trail. Highlights are the many tamarisk trees planted as windbreaks beginning in the mid-1800's. They flower in spring and summer producing lovely pink spikes at the ends of branches. The rocks are home to sea ox-eye and occasionally some naturalized ice plant. Naturalized chicory with its blue flowers can also be seen. Watch for longtails entering their nests along here as well. Shelly Bay is a low energy, shallow beach that has a playground and snack bar. The Railway Trail does continue beyond Shelly Bay but there is a break in it where some development has occurred. Walk up North Shore Rd. and turn left into Burchall Cove where the trail continues. The Bermuda Railway Museum located along the Trail presents a history of Bermuda's Railway.

*Directions: Take bus # 10 or 11. Get off at either Shelly Bay or the Bermuda Railway Museum. If you get off at Shelly Bay walk southwest, heading toward Flatts Village. If you begin at the Railway Museum, head northeast toward Shelly Bay. Scooters can be parked at either location.*

# Scurvy Grass or Sea Rocket

*Cakile lanceolata*
Family: Cruciferae

Native Herb

**Found on Clearwater Beach and South Shore Park**

Scurvy grass is found just above the high tide line on beaches and on coastal rocks. This plant masters life near the sea with its thick (succulent), toothed leaves and ability to germinate quickly. Stems may be erect or horizontally spread and branching. Lower leaves are larger and more broadly oblong than upper leaves. Lower leaf edges are also more coarsely indented than those on the upper leaves. Leaf attachment to stem can be opposite or alternate. Tiny, four-petaled white or light-purplish flowers are found at the end of stems. Flowers are produced from spring to autumn. Seeds are contained in tiny pods that are well designed for floating in water. Leaves are edible though it is best to allow them to remain on the beach where they help hold down the sand. Scurvy grass is not found in great quantities here so enjoy its beauty.

Height - 15-75 cm          Lower leaf - 5-7.5 cm long          Flower - 0.5-1.5 cm diameter          Seed pod - 2-2.5 cm long

# Iodine Bush or Bay Lavender

*Mallotonia gnaphalodes*
Family: Boraginaceae

Native Herb or Shrub

**Found on the dunes of Warwick Long Bay**

Common on sandy beaches and coastal rocks, this plant has silvery-green thick but soft leaves that are covered with tiny white hairs. The leaves are elongated ovals that narrow at the end nearest to the stem. They attach to the stem in alternate positions, circling the stem. The plant is found in clumps. Clusters of white flowers, some with deep red markings, form on spikes curving outward near the top of the plant. The flowers are produced on just one side of the curved spike. Each flower has 5 rounded petals and can be seen from spring to fall. Some flowers have been observed in winter, however they are abundant during spring and summer. Fruits are oval and black with 2 nutlets.

Height - to 1.3 m          Leaf - 1.5-10 cm long          Flower - 3mm diameter          Fruit - 0.3-0.5 cm

# Beach Lobelia or Inkberry

*Scaevola plumieri*
Family: Goodeniaceae

Native Herb or Shrub

**Found on the dunes of Warwick Long Bay and Nonsuch Island**

Beach lobelia is a common perennial herb found on South Shore dunes, fairly close to the water. This succulent shrub bears shiny, leathery oval leaves on branching stems. The leaves have smooth margins and alternate in their attachment to the stem. They look like small paddles. A 5-petaled white flower with a yellow center highlights this deep green sprawling herb. Flowers are produced from spring to autumn. It produces a juicy, black oval berry, which explains its common name of Inkberry. It is not as common as it used to be due to competition from Pacific Lobelia.

Height - to 0.5m          Leaf - 4-9 cm long          Flower - ≈2.5 cm tall          Berry - 0.7-2 cm long

# Pacific Lobelia or Beach Naupaka or Hailstones

*Scaevola taccada*
Family: Goodeniaceae

Herb of Unknown Origin

**Found on the dunes of Warwick Long Bay**

Seed of Pacific
Lobelia

This invasive relative of the native Beach Lobelia (*S. plumieri*) is found on sandy dunes, close to the water. It is a succulent shrub whose leaves are a bit larger than *S. plumieri* and can be easily distinguished by its white fleshy berry (drupe) seen during late summer and fall. The outer edges (margins) of its leaves have slight indentations. The leaves attach in circular whorls around the stem. The stem is woody nearer to the sand, and does continue underground. The white flowers are produced in clusters in the axil of the leaves. The flowers are produced in groups of three and have a yellow central region. They have 5 petals that form a semi or half circle around the center of the flower. It was not described by Britton in 1918 thus is likely a recent arrival to the Island.[5] The nickname hailstones refers to the appearance of the fruit.

Height - to 0.5m in Bermuda (reportedly taller in other parts of the world)
Flower - 2 cm long petals

Leaf - to 15 cm long; to 7 cm wide
Fruit - 1-1.7 cm long

# Coast Spurge

*Chamaesyce mesembrianthemifolia*
Synonyms: *Euphorbia mesembrianthemifolia, Chamaesyce buxifolia*
Family: Euphorbiaceae

Native Herb

**Found on Warwick Long Bay and Clearwater Beach**

Right: Coast spurge with leaves folded close to stem or branch to conserve water
Below: Coast spurge with leaves spread open to capture maximum solar energy

A perennial found growing in coastal rocks and beaches, this low-growing plant has branching stems with small leaves that form opposite each other. The leaves are oval but come to a point and are somewhat fleshy. The green leaves are sometimes reddish in certain areas, as are the stems. Stems often lie flat on the ground as a vine, with parts or the end becoming more erect. The leaves can bend in toward the stem, perhaps to conserve water. Flowers have 4 tiny white petals and are produced at upper leaf-stem axils throughout the year. Another common name is coastal beach sandmat.

Height (stem) - 17-70 cm          Leaf - 0.8-1.2 cm long          Flower - tiny

# Blodgett's Spurge

*Euphorbia blodgettii or Chamaesyce blodgettii*
Family: Euphorbiaceae

Native Herb

**Found on Warwick Long Bay beach and other South Shore beaches**

This spurge is another low-growing (almost vine-like) perennial found on beaches and coastal rocks. It is delicate looking as one observes it against the sand. Blodgett's Spurge is distinguished from Coast Spurge by its oblong, more roundish leaves that are in groups along the stem. These leaves are separated by more empty space than seen in Coast Spurge. There are branches coming from the stem that range from 10-40 cm long. Stems often lie flat on the ground as a vine, with parts or the end becoming more erect. Leaves are very slightly scalloped near their tip. Flowers are produced at leaf axil, nearly throughout the year, and are white or slightly colored with 4 petals. Tiny round seed capsules are formed after flowering.

Height - 10-40 cm long stems                    Leaf - to 0.5 cm long                    Flower - tiny

# Sea Purslane

*Sesuvium portulacastrum*
Family: Portulacaceae

Native Herb

**Found on Clearwater Beach and Whalebone Bay**

This sprawling succulent's thick leaves and stems serve it well in the dune or rock environment it inhabits. Its very shiny appearance is due to a waxy coating that serves to protect the plant from drying out. It looks like it was coated with sunscreen because it is so shiny. Rich green and sometimes red are the colors of its leaves and stem. It successfully lives in rocky crevices and sand. Its small pink or purplish flowers are shaped like a funnel, have five petals (almost star-like), and grow from the axils of some of the leaves.

Height - 5-8 cm, length - to 2 m          Leaf - 1-6 cm          Flower - up to 1 cm diameter

# Seaside Morning Glory

*Ipomoea pes-caprae*
Family: Convolvulaceae

Native Vine

**Found on the dunes at Warwick Long Bay, Clearwater Beach, Whalebone Bay**

This perennial vine bearing large, stiff, rounded (with a notch at apex), green leaves is often seen sprawling down sandy dunes. Branching stems creep horizontally along the sand, sometimes 20 meters long. The leaf stems (petiole) may be reddish in color. The leaves alternate positions along the stem. Purple to pink showy flowers grow from the base of leaves. The flowers are produced from July through November, however if the plant is in a protected location, it may flower at other times as well.

Length (vine) - to 20 m long          Leaf - 5-10 cm broad          Flower corolla - ≈5 cm long, 5-7 cm broad

31

# Woody Glasswort

*Salicornia perennis*
Family: Chenopodiaceae

Native Herb

**Found along Ferry Reach near Blue Hole Park**

Above: Woody glasswort and flowering sea lavender

This sturdy and unique plant is common in salt marshes and in coastal sands and rocks. It has a stem that is prostrate, lying horizontally along the ground. Upright jointed branches arise from the stem. They contain tightly compressed scales that are reduced leaves. These scale-like leaves form opposite each other. Inconspicuous white flowers are produced in the upper scales during the spring and summer.

Height - 20 to 30 cm  (did not observe any to this height, though others have recorded this)    Leaf - reduced to scales    Flower - tiny

# Sea Lavender

*Limonium carolinianum*
Synonym: *Limonium nashii*
Family: Plumbaginaceae

Native Herb

**Found along Ferry Reach near Blue Hole Park**

Sea lavender flowers beautify any marsh or mangrove area they inhabit. It can be found near the shore around parts of Castle Harbor and Ferry Reach. Its deep green leaves are elongated ovals, but narrow to a point near the leaf apex (tip). Leaves may have slight undulations along their margins. The leaves are produced at the base of the plant in a circle around the stem. Smooth green stems arise from the center of the leaves and hold the clusters (panicles) of tiny, pale lavender flowers. These flower clusters appear almost stiff and can be dried for long lasting beauty. The flowers have 5 petals and stand upright from their base. Flowers are produced in late summer and autumn.

Height - to 0.75 m               Leaf - 5-18 cm long               Flowers - tiny

# Beach Croton or Seaside Croton

*Croton punctatus*
Family: Euphorbiaceae

Native Herb or Shrub

**Found on Clearwater Beach**

Seed capsule enclosing seeds

Beach Croton interspersed with seaside morning glory

Beach Croton is a sturdy perennial shrub found in sandy environments. A large stand exists on Clearwater Beach. It grows a bit taller the further inland it is from the high tide line. The leaf surface is covered with short, whitish or light colored hairs. Leaves have smooth margins and can be elliptical, oblong or oval in shape. The stem is silvery grey and has fine hairs on it. The leaves have a texture similar to felt. It flowers spring to autumn, producing tiny flowers in clusters found at the top of the plant. The flowers are a creamy white color.

Height - 0.5-1.0 m                    Leaf - to 6 cm long                    Flower - 1-2 cm diameter

# Spanish Bayonet

*Yucca aloifolia*
Family: Agavaceae

Native Herb

**Found near Whalebone Bay and Warwick Long Bay**

The Spanish bayonet is commonly seen on sandy dunes and hillsides, especially on the South Shore. This succulent is easy to spot with its long pointed thick leaves that remind one of a bayonet. The bayonet-like leaves form a circle around the stem. It frequently grows in colonies. Touching the "bayonet" could hurt, as the leaf margins have spiny, serrated edges that can cut and end in a sharp point. A mass of creamy white flowers form a cluster (panicle) at the top of a tall spike (to >2 m) in the center of the leaves. Flowers are produced from spring to autumn.

Height - to 3.5 m                    Leaf - to 70 m                    Flower panicle (cluster) - to 0.75 m

# Seaside Heliotrope

*Heliotropium curassavicum*
Family: Boraginaceae

Native Herb

**Found in Walsingham Nature Reserve**

This annual herb is found along sandy shores and in salt marshes. Its foliage appears greenish-white, fleshy, and loosely spreading. Leaves are linear or oblong-linear and margins are entire. Flowers are produced on a spike that splits in two parts (v-shaped) that coil away from each other. Flower color is white with a yellow eye that may change to blue, and the tiny flowers have 5 petals each. One spike may have more than 20 tiny flowers. Flowers are produced from spring to autumn.

Height - 10-48 cm                    Leaf - 2-5 cm                    Flower spike - 5-7 cm

# Yellow Bermuda Bean or Vigna

*Vigna luteola*
Family: Fabaceae

Vine of Unknown Origin

**Found in Cooper's Island Nature Reserve**

Vigna is found on coastal hillsides, roadsides, and dunes. It is a perennial vine with lanceolate shaped leaves (shaped like a lance, narrowing at the tip) that are dark green and stiff. Britton reports the leaf shape as sometimes being oval, however this has not been observed.[5] The distinctive yellow flowers form in clusters at the ends of stems. The flowers are produced year round though more are seen from spring to autumn. These turn into pods ranging from 3-7 cm long.

Length (vine) - to 3 m                    Leaf - ≈5 cm long                    Flower - ≈2 cm long

# Key West Gentian or Seaside Gentian

*Eustoma exaltatum*
Family: Gentianaceae

Herb of Unknown Origin

**Found in Cooper's Island Nature Reserve and Clearwater Beach**

This pretty, purple flower is a recent arrival to Bermuda. It can be found growing from limestone rock, sand, or along roadsides. It is seen in areas near the airport, such as Cooper's Island, St. David's Island, and Nonsuch Island and seems to be spreading island-wide in the coastal areas. David Wingate suggests its seeds may have arrived in the landing gear of an airplane.[27] Its leaves are oblong and opposite, with smooth margins. They clasp the stem, having no stalk (petiole). They are a soft or light-green color. The flower forms on a tall stem, usually solitary, one flower per stem. There are five pale-purple petals that encircle a darker purple center. Five bright-yellow stamen and two green stigma are in the center of the flower. The flowers are produced mainly from July through November.

Height - 30-90 cm                    Leaf - to 7.5 cm long                    Flower - 4 cm

# Prickly Pear

*Opuntia stricta var. dillenii*
Family: Cactaceae

Native Cactus

**Found along Railway Trail near Whalebone Bay, on dunes of Warwick Long Bay, Spittal Pond Nature Reserve**

Fruit-laden prickly pear cactus with seaside daisy (*Wedelia*) vines growing over it

Prickly Pear are easy to spot as they are a cactus with thick, rounded, branching segments, sometimes called pads. Touch with care as the small bristles (glochids) penetrate the skin but do not come out easily because they are barbed. Longer pointed spines are easy to spot on the fleshy plant skin. A beautiful yellow solitary flower about 2-3 cm across is produced in summer and autumn. This evolves into a reddish-purple, spiny, ovoid fruit 5-7.5 cm long which is edible. Carefully peel before ingesting, as fruit is protected by glochids. Rubbing a cloth or soaking in cold water will remove some spines from the fruit. Peel it with care, wearing gloves is suggested. The fruit is quite sweet. The green part of the cactus (pads) can also be eaten, after being peeled and cooked.

Height - 0.5-1.5 m                    Flower - 7.5 cm broad                    Fruit - 5-7.5 cm long

# Seaside Evening Primrose

*Oenothera humifusa*
Family: Onagraceae

Native Herb

**Found on the roadside just before reaching Clearwater Beach**

Primrose turns orange as the day progresses

Plant blooms at night as a yellow flower... still yellow in the morning

Found inhabiting sand dunes or grassy areas near sandy beaches, this low-lying species produces a silvery-green hairy leaf. The leaves are thick and felt-like. Leaf shape varies with some leaves showing more indentations than others. There may be a single point at the end of the leaf and more sharp points down the side of each leaf. The seaside evening primrose can become more shrubby in winter. The four-petaled yellow flowers bloom at night. They turn orange as the day progresses. Sometimes plants have different colored flowers, some yellow, others orange at the same time. The flowers are produced in the upper leaf axils from summer to autumn. It was seen by Britton on "sandy hills and sandy shores, St. David's Island, Castle Point, near Tucker's Town and Southampton."[5]

Height - 10-50 cm                    Leaf - 1-5 cm long                    Flower - 1-2.5 cm long

# Beach Evening Primrose

*Oenothera drummondii*
Family: Onagraceae

Herb of Unknown Origin

**Found in South Shore Park**

This sprawling herb is found in sand environments, thriving where protected from the wind and heavy salt spray. Leaves are a soft green, felt-like in texture, and all show smooth margins, unlike the Dunes Evening Primrose (*Oenothera humifusa*) with its more acutely cut leaf margins. The leaves are covered with tiny, fine hairs. They form opposite each other, alternating as they rise up the stem so all leaves are maximally exposed to the sun. Near the end of the stem the leaves appear to form a circle around the stem. The leaves are larger in size the lower their position on the stem. Stems often become woody in winter. Flowers are bright yellow and have four petals and eight large stamen. They are produced between the leaves near the end of the stems or branches. Other resources have not documented *O. drummondii* as being present in Bermuda. The fact that all of the leaf margins are smooth is justification for this identification, however further research may be appropriate to confirm the identification.

Height - ≈12 cm high; stem length to ≈1 m long          Leaf - to 7 cm long          Flower petal - to 3 cm long

# Sea Ox-eye

*Borrichia arborescens*
Family: Compositae

Native Shrub

**Found at Warwick Long Bay, Cooper's Island Nature Reserve, Blue Hole Park, Whalebone Bay**

Sea Ox-eye is a dense, branching coastal shrub, found frequently on rocky hillsides. Its branches are woody. Height can vary depending on location and it can spread horizontally for more than a meter. Foliage is unique as it comes in two colors, deep green and silver-grey-green. Both colors can be found on the same plant, or on separate plants that may be near each other. Succulent leaves are oval in shape with smooth edges. They are oppositely placed on the branches. Flowers are daisy-like with bright yellow petals and orange centers. It flowers from spring to winter, and the flowers attract butterflies.

Height - 0.3-2 m (has been observed taller)          Leaf - 2.5-7 cm. long          Flower - 2.5 cm broad

# Bay Grape

*Coccoloba uvifera*
Family: Polygonaceae

Native Tree

**Found on all walks**

Sometimes called Sea Grape, this native tree adapts well to rocky coastal conditions by growing from the limestone rock in whatever form nature dictates. The tree is sometimes broader than tall, with branch diameter ranging from 5-18 cm. It usually has multiple trunks grouped together. The color of the trunk is a mottled light-grey and tan, with a fairly smooth texture. It is also found in upland areas showing more uniform shape, growing up to 10 m. The leaves are shiny, have smooth margins, and are highlighted by red veins. They have a round shape, and are strong and leathery. Leaves have been used as plates and wedding invitations. The leaves are alternately arranged on branches. The tree is evergreen, with leaves falling and being replaced throughout the year. Flowers are small white or light-green spikes that produce a small grape-like purple (when ripe) fruit. Flowers are produced from spring to autumn. Britton reports that "fruit edible but not very palatable."[5]

Height - 10 m                    Leaf - 5-18 cm diameter                    Flower - 10-30 cm long clusters (racemes)

# Buttonwood

*Conocarpus erectus*
Family: Combretaceae

Native Tree

**Found on all walks**

This native mangrove is a mainstay on the rocky coasts of Bermuda. It succeeds by being flexible, sometimes becoming a tall tree, other times a sprawling woody shrub. The forms it can take would inspire any bonsai gardener. Its thick, leathery, green leaves are salt tolerant. Leaves are oval to elliptical and smooth around the edges. It is sometimes confused with olivewood but the buttonwood's leaf margins are always smooth, with no indentations. New leaves are produced after the winter. Buttonwood produces a greenish, funnel-like flower in a cluster in late spring and summer. Purplish seeds are grouped together at leaf axils and are 1.5-2.5 cm long. An introduced buttonwood with silvery, felt-like leaves also exists in Bermuda. It is more shrub-like and matures to produce a rounded shape. In the past, the bark of the native buttonwood had been used for tanning but this was halted due to a decrease in the buttonwood population.

Height - 1.5-10 m                         Leaf - 2.5-5 cm long                         Flower clusters (racemes) - 2.5-5 cm long

# Seaside Goldenrod

*Solidago sempervirens*
Family: Compositae

Native Herb

**Found near Spittal Pond, Warwick Long Bay, Alfred Blackburn Smith Audubon Reserve, North Shore Railway Trail**

Growing to 1.5 m high, this tall "weed" bears bright-green, long, thin (lanceolate), pointed, alternate leaves that encircle the stem. Lower leaves are more rounded than upper leaves. The leaves are somewhat thickened. A terminal mass (panicle) of bright yellow flowers may be seen in June but is most commonly observed in late summer and fall in many habitats. Surprisingly, it grows well on both sand dunes as well as in a substrate containing more soil.

Height - 0.4-1.5+ m          Leaf - lower can be 20 cm long          Flower (panicle) height - 7.5-15 cm

# Tassel Plant

*Suriana maritima*
Family: Surianaceae

Native Shrub

**Found at Warwick Long Bay and Cooper's Island Nature Reserve**

Often seen in rocky coastal and beach habitats, this evergreen shrub has thick narrow leaves up to 5 cm long that form tight clusters around the stem. Leaf shape is linear-spatulate. Leaf margins are smooth and the leaf is covered with tiny hairs. Small yellow flowers are produced in spring and summer, comprised of 5 petals and 5 green sepals that form a star-like shape around the more curved petals. It is somewhat similar to Iodine Bush (*Mallatonia*) but it is a taller plant, with shorter leaves and very different flowers. The stem is woody and quite sturdy.

Height - 1.5+ m          Leaf - 1- 5 cm long          Fruit - 0.8-1.2 cm broad          Flower - ≈2 cm diameter

# Coast Sophora

*Sophora tomentosa*
Family: Leguminosae

Native Herb

**Found at Spittal Pond Nature Reserve and Warwick Long Bay**

The brilliant yellow flowers identify this shrub, which is often seen along the rocky shores of Bermuda. They are produced in spring and summer. The flowers are formed in a spike-like cluster at the end of stems and are outstanding to view. They complement the interesting leaf shape and color. Leaves are compound meaning each leaf is made up of smaller leaflets. Leaves alternate along the stem. Leaflets are opposite each other along the leaf axis and oval in shape. Color of leaves can vary from dark-green to silvery-green and have small wooly hairs. Seed pods of this member of the bean family are constricted around each seed in the pod. The plant may develop into a woody shrub.

Height - 1-3 m (rarely this tall in Bermuda)     Leaf -10-17.5 cm     Flower cluster (raceme)- 10-40 cm

47

# Bermudiana

*Sisyrinchium bermudiana*
Family: Iridacea

Endemic Herb

Found at Cooper's Island Nature Reserve and Warwick Long Bay

Usually finished flowering by mid-June, this endemic beauty grows from rock or sand just back from the shore as well as in some inland locales. The elongated blade-like lower leaves envelop the flower's stem. The flower grows on its own stem and has shorter leaves. It flowers a luscious purple color from April to June. There are several flowers at the end of the stalk, usually flowering one at a time. The flower has six petals surrounding a yellow center. It is considered to be the national flower of Bermuda.

Height - ≈25-50 cm               Leaf (basal) - 10-30 cm               Flower - petals-1.2-2 cm long

# Bay Bean

*Canavali lineata*
Family: Leguminosae

Native Vine

Found **at Warwick Long Bay and Clearwater Beach**

Growing along sandy beaches, this branching vine bears leathery leaves arranged in threes. Leaves are oval but more rounded at their base. Margins are smooth (entire). A pretty pink flower is produced by this sprawling vine in racemes at the end of their own stem. The flowers have two major parts whose shape is like a kidney bean. The flowers produce pods that contain brown, oblong beans. These pods allow the Bay Bean to colonize new environments, sometimes traveling many miles in the sea. According to Lefroy, this plant was mentioned in written documents as early as 1623.[17]

Length - 1-8 meters          Leaf - 2-10 cm long          Flower - ≈2.0-2.5 cm length          Seed Pods - to 7 cm long

# Wild Poinsettia or Joseph's Coat

*Euphorbia heterophylla*
Family: Euphorbiaceae

Native Herb

**Found at Whalebone Bay, Cooper's Island Nature Reserve, Spittal Pond, Warwick Long Bay**

This eye-catching herb is found on both rocky and sandy hills just inland from dunes. The variation in leaf shape is huge. Some leaves are long and thin, lance-shaped, with small teeth while others are oval to round in shape. Many of the more oval/round leaves have symmetrical indentations in the leaf edges, almost looking like an oak leaf. Leaves are alternately placed on the stem. The lower leaves are green. On the upper leaves, there is a central area that is a brilliant red, in a shape similar to the long thin oval-shaped leaf. The flower of this plant is tiny, produced throughout the year, and located in the very center of the upper, red and green leaves. The flower color is pale green.

Height - 0.33-1.33 m                    Leaf - to 6 cm long                    Flower - tiny

# Lantana or Common Sage Bush

*Lantana involucrata*
Family: Verbenaceae

Naturalized Shrub

**Found growing on hills above Warwick Long Bay, Alfred Blackburn Smith Audubon Reserve, Nonsuch Island**

This is a common, introduced sage bush. Stems and leaf undersides are covered with tiny hairs. The fragrant leaves are oval or elliptical with edges bearing small rounded indentations that are scalloped in appearance. Flowers are a pale pinkish-purple (sometimes nearly white) and are produced in a tight umbel on stems that may reach 5 cm in length. The flowers are seen year round and produce a small green fruit that turns black. It looks like a berry and is poisonous. In Britton's (1918) time, it was considered the most abundant shrub of Bermuda and reportedly was introduced pre-1800 for use as firewood. This seems odd as the bush does not produce enough wood to make it valuable in this way.[5] This is not the sage used in cooking. It is now considered more of an invasive.

Height - 0.60-1.6m                    Leaf - 1.2-3.75 cm long                    Flower - 0.6-1cm tall

# Bermuda Olivewood

*Cassine laneana*
Family: Celastraceae

Endemic Tree

**Found in Cooper's Island Nature Reserve, Blue Hole Park, Nonsuch Island**

This is an endemic evergreen bearing elliptical, leathery leaves. The trunk averages 7 m tall while the rest of the height comes from very upright branches. The trunk is a light brownish-gray and fairly smooth. The silhouette of this tree is oval making it an outstanding landscape plant. The leaf margins have small undulations (which distinguish them from buttonwood) and are dark green on both sides, though a bit shinier on the upper surface. Flowers are produced in late winter and early spring in tiny light-green or yellowish-white clusters at the leaf axils. Fruits are solitary or 2-4 together, yellowish-white and rounded. The wood is very dense and the tree grows slowly. Seeds are a favorite food of rats, thus it has been difficult for this tree to maintain itself.[5] Planting young trees is a good way to deal with this problem.

Height - 8-14 m          Leaf - 5-10 cm long          Fruit - 2.5 cm long          Flower - tiny

# Seaside Daisy

*Wedelia trilobata*
Family: Compositae

Naturalized Vine

**Found in Cooper's Island Nature Reserve and Warwick Long Bay**

Found on coastal hillsides, this groundcover has taken over many areas, and is also known as the Creeping Daisy. It is an invasive species, as it aggressively prevents natives from living in their environment and spreads rapidly. Its stems cover the ground like wires that bear dense green foliage and brightly-colored yellow flowers. Flowers are produced primarily in the summer however some can be seen in spring, fall and occasionally winter. It usually dies back with salt burn in the winter, looking less vibrant.[27] Bright-green leaves are elliptically shaped with dentate (toothed) blade margins (edges). *Wedelia* was not recorded by Britton in his 1918 book on the *Flora of Bermuda*, and it is believed to have been recently introduced.

Height - to 30 cm                    Leaf - 5-10 cm blade length                    Flower - ≈2.5 cm diameter

# Wild Stock

*Matthiola incana*   Britton: *Microstigma inca*
Family: Cruciferae

Naturalized Herb

**Found at Warwick Long Bay, along the South Shore, Nonsuch Island**

Wild Stock was introduced and has spread, especially along the South Shore. This shrub blooms a vibrant magenta in spring and early summer, which makes it easy to identify. Though unusual, it has been seen flowering in January. The flowers have four purple petals surrounding a small white center and bloom in clusters. When not blooming, its features include leaves which are long ovals with blunt ends, smooth margins (edges) and a silvery-green color. The leaves are soft and felt-like. Long, narrow seed pods evolve from the flowers. Lefroy stated in 1884, "to be found, but not abundantly, among the rocks along the southern shore, in Warwick Parish. Probably escaped from gardens."[17]

Height - 0.75 m or less                    Leaf - 5-15 cm                    Flower (cluster) - 10-12.5 cm tall

# Oleander

*Nerium oleander*
Family: Apocynaceae

Naturalized Shrub

**Found enroute to all walks and on the dunes of Warwick Long Bay**

This introduced shrub is large and has long, narrow leathery leaves. It is found along rocky coastlines, and occasionally on upper dune areas. Oleander is planted in many inland locations as it forms beautiful hedges. The leaves form opposite one another on the stem. To insure that all leaves receive the most light, leaves are positioned on the stem so they are rarely directly above or below another set of leaves. Oleander requires soil, though this can be sandy. It's loaded with large clusters of pink or peach flowers that catch the eye. More colors have been cultivated. Some plants bear single flowers, other plants have double flowers. Flowers have five petals each and can be seen from spring through December, though best in spring and summer. Long pods form containing seeds. Ironically the vegetative matter of this beautiful plant is poisonous when ingested.

Height - 2.75-7 m          Leaf - 7.5-13 cm long          Flower - to 9 cm long, 4 cm across          Pod - 10-15 cm long

# Fennel

*Foeniculum vulgare*
Family: Umbelliferae

Naturalized Herb

**Found on all walks**

Just rub your fingers on this plant, smell them, and you'll know for sure it's fennel. The fragrance is unmistakable and pleasant. This herb can be used in cooking such as in stews and soups and it may have been introduced to Bermuda for just that reason. It is found in marshes, both rocky and sandy hills near the shoreline, and is a widely dispersed weed. Fennel's many thin, feather-like leaves have little surface area to minimize evaporation, making it quite successful. Each little leaflet is 1.5-2 cm long. The leaflets connect to the main stem with a clasping petiole (stem). At the top of some stems, umbels are produced, that is a yellow umbrella-like cluster of tiny flowers. It flowers in summer and autumn.

Height - 0.75-1.3 m          Leaf - 1.5-2 cm long          Flower cluster (umbel) - 10-12 cm across

# Asparagus Fern

*Asparagus densiflorus 'Sprengeri'*
Family: Liliaceae

Naturalized Herb

**Found on all walks**

This evergreen perennial grows prolifically in Bermuda, after being introduced by man. Not a true fern, this member of the lily family grows densely in many habitats, and is saltwater tolerant. Its mounds of foliage can go on for several meters. The leaves are small, needle-like, and interspersed with tiny thorns. Color ranges from dark green to a light green. It produces tiny clusters of white, fragrant flowers that mature into red berries. Part of its success is due to the dispersion of these seeds (berries) by birds. It is considered an invasive species.

Height - to 1m                    Leaf - 1 cm long                    Flower - 7 mm diameter

# Seashore Rush Grass

*Sporobolus virginicus*
Family: Gramineae

Native Grass

**Found on dunes of Warwick Long Bay, Clearwater Beach, Nonsuch Island**

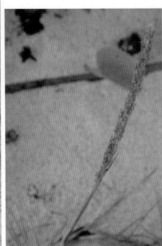

Seashore rush grass is a stabilizing grass found on dunes, mangrove edges, and salt marshes. It can best be identified by its flowers which form a light tan single spike. It sends leaf blades upright and also sends out "wire-like" runners that cover sand dunes, sending their roots into the sand along the way. More leaves shoot upward from these runners. It forms dense clumps of grass whose stems are at first upright, then may become prostrate. The runners that look like wire enable it to spread vegetatively. This works effectively as a form of reproduction and a sand stabilizer. Leaves have a sheath at their base that overlaps the stem. Leaf blades are nearly opposite and have pointed tips. The flowers are dense, single spikes. They are produced on stems up to 40 cm tall in summer and fall.

Height - 15-75 cm                    Leaf - 2.5-20 cm long, 2 mm wide                    Flower - 2.5-7.5 cm long, 1mm-1cm wide

# Southern Burr Grass

*Cenchrus tribuloides*
Family: Gramineae

Native Grass

**Found on dunes of Warwick Long Bay**

Found growing on sand dunes, this grass flowers from spring to autumn. It is among the grasses that help hold down the dunes, preventing coastal erosion. The stems are at first erect, then flatten out into mats with many branches. Leaf blades are compressed, flat and end in a point. It is named for a spiky burr head. The head holds small pointed burrs that will hurt if stepped on and can easily stick to clothing or shoes and aid in seed dispersal. They are light-green to tan in color. The burr has small hairs as well as spines that can break off and become imbedded in the skin, causing great discomfort.

Height - stems are 20-75 cm        Leaf - 6-10 cm long, ≈2-3 mm wide        Flower (spikes) - 2.5-5 cm long        Burrs - 1-1.5 cm

# Salt Grass

*Spartina patens*
Family: Gramineae

Native Grass

**Found at Cooper's Island Nature Reserve, Warwick Long Bay, Nonsuch Island**

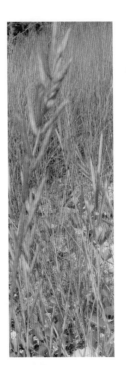

This species of perennial grass has the ability to survive in a salt-water environment. Its roots can be covered with salt water and the plant carries on. It is found along dunes, marshes and rocky shores. It can live where other plants cannot, due to roots that can block salt absorption, and leaves that can excrete salt. It is seen in clumps or solitary, with tall, upright stems. Leaf blades are 0.5 to 5 mm wide and are rolled to form rounded structures but edges are rough. The rolling helps to conserve water. Flowers appear as spikes in summer and autumn.

Height - 1.2 to 1.5 m          Leaf - 15-75 cm long, 0.5-5 mm wide          Flower - Spikes to 18 cm long

# Sheathed Paspalum

*Paspalum vaginatum*
Family: Gramineae

Native Grass

**Found on all walks**

Sheathed Paspalum is a common grass that is found near dunes and marshes. It stabilizes the earth through an extensive underground stem (rhizome) network. The rootstock is extremely strong. Leaves are narrow with the base of each leaf forming a compressed and overlapping sheath-like structure that encircles the stem. The leaves may have some tiny hairs at their base. Their tips are pointed. Flowers are produced at the end of a leafy stem in two spikes. Flowers are produced in summer and autumn. Observing the flowers is the best way to identify this grass.

Height - Stems are 20-75 cm        Leaf - to15 cm long, 6-8 mm wide        Flowering spike - to 6 cm long, 1-2 mm wide

# West Indian Grass

*Eustachys petraea*
Family: Gramineae

Naturalized Grass

**Found along hill tops near Warwick Long Bay**

This perennial grass is identified best by its flowering spikes, which are about 7 cm long. The spikes can range in number from 3 to 6 per stalk, an important distinguishing feature. They are produced from spring to autumn. The stalks containing the flower arise from a plant whose leaves are primarily at the base of the plant, near the ground. The leaf blades vary in that some have more rounded ends, while others are pointed. The height of this plant varies depending on where it is located. The further inland from a sandy beach, the taller it grows. It has been observed growing in sand but seems to thrive in soil along paths, roadsides, and near other vegetation.

Height - 55-60 cm tall                Leaf - 13+ cm long                Flower - spikes to 7 cm long, ≈2mm wide

# Switch Grass

*Panicum virgatum*
Family: Gramineae

Native Grass

**Found along the Railway Trail near Whalebone Bay and Cooper's Island Nature Reserve**

This tall grass is found near sandy shores and along rocky coastal areas. It has wide leaves (relative to other grasses mentioned in this book) and a graceful panicle (spike with angled spikelets arising from its sides). The panicle is a tan color. These flowers are produced in the summer or autumn. The leaves alternate along the stem, on the stems bearing the flowers (panicles) as well as the stems just bearing leaves. Leaves come to a point at the end and have a wide mid-rib running the length of the leaf blade. The leaf blades often arc (curve) gracefully outward when they get to be about 40 cm long. This grass grows in clumps, and may exist as an isolated clump in a given location.

Height - to 2 m          Leaf - to 50 cm long, 1.5 cm wide          Flower (Cluster or Panicle) - 12-50 cm

63

# St. Augustine Grass

*Stenotaphrum secundatum*
Family: Gramineae

Native Grass

**Found on most lawns, entry to most nature reserves**

(above) St. Augustine grass at entrance to Spittal Pond Nature Reserve

This perennial grass, sometimes referred to as crab grass, forms dense mats, is fairly salt tolerant, spreads quickly and is quite hardy. It is found along marshes, in some coastal areas, and on most Bermudian lawns. Leaf blades are succulent with a blunt and rounded tip. The leaf blades are flattened and bend outward. Flowers are produced throughout the year. The flowers are produced as single spikes at the end of a stem or lateral branch.

Height - up to 25 cm long          Leaf - 1.5-15 cm long, 1mm-1cm wide          Flower - 3-4 cm tall

# Sharp Rush

*Juncus acutus*
Family: Juncaceae

Naturalized Rush

**Found along Ferry Reach near Blue Hole Park**

This distinctive rush is tall, dark-green with sharp-pointed stiff stems and leaves. The stems and leaves are also cylindrical, the only difference is that the stems have flowers or fruits off to the side at their top. The tufted clumps of tall grass can be found near marshes and coastlines, generally damp areas with muddy or sandy substrates. It is a perennial and can spread by seed or underground stem. The flowers are tiny but are produced in clusters of 5-8 and become light brownish-orange oval seeds that are about 0.5 cm long. Seeds are surrounded by tepals, which are triangular, darker brown structures that seem to hold the seed in place.

Height - 0.60-1.5 m          Leaf - ≈ 1m tall, 2-4 mm diameter          Seed capsules - 5mm long          Flower - tiny; panicle - 3-23 cm

# Bermuda Cedar

*Juniperus bermudiana*
Family: Cupressaceae

Endemic Tree

**Found on all walks**

Above: Older cedar in Walsingham Reserve

Above: Young cedar at BIOS

An endemic tree (actually a juniper, not a cedar) found on rocky shores and upland forests. In 1918 Britton reported it as "the most abundant and characteristic tree of Bermuda."[5] It is now considered critically endangered due to defoliation produced by several different scale insects beginning in the 1930's, through the 1950's. It was once the dominant tree of the Bermuda forests. Over 90% of the cedars were destroyed by 1954.[2] Those that survived were cultivated and thanks to the work of the Bermuda Conservation Dept., have been (and continue to be) reestablished throughout the Island. The tree holds up well in high winds and its wood is valued for strength and resistance to rot. The roots of the cedar are able to live securely in the limestone rock. Early settlers used it for boat building among other applications and nearly cleared it from the Island. One of the first conservation laws of Bermuda (and the New World) was to limit its use, enacted in 1622.[19] Beautiful silver berries form on the evergreen scale-like leaves. The young tree is conic in shape. The mature tree top is rounded and wider than that of younger trees. The tree is irregularly shaped, sometimes with branches wider than high. Flowers are produced in March and April, giving the trees a "golden appearance which adds much to their beauty."[17] Fruit (silvery-blue berries) is seen in summer and fall. A beautiful older cedar can be seen in Walsingham Reserve.

Height - to 15 m                    Leaf - 1-5 mm long                    Leaf branch - 1.3-1.6 mm wide

# Casuarina or Australian Whistling Pine

*Casuarina equisetifolia*
Family: Casuarinaceae

Naturalized Tree

**Found on all walks**

This tall, widely seen tree has long needles and whistles given enough wind. The deep-green, scale-like needles arise singly from the branches. It comes from Australia and was aggressively planted in the mid-twentieth century as a fast growing windbreak when the endemic Bermuda cedar was nearly destroyed by insect infestation. It was thought that it would hold up well in hurricanes, but did not fare well under high winds, blowing over instead. The hurricanes do succeed in disseminating the cones, which release seeds from which new *Casuarina* plants arise. The *Casuarina* is found growing from rocks along the coastlines and in sandy soils, thriving in these environments. Male flowers produce reddish catskins and female flowers produce tiny wooden cones that remain on the tree for several months, then cover the ground. The plant is wind pollinated, not needing insects for this task. The trunk is light-grey with some tan areas and relatively smooth in texture. It is considered an invasive as it reproduces rapidly and in large numbers, takes away the habitat of other native plants, with nothing able to grow under it.

Height - to 24 m          Leaf - 10-13 cm long          Cones - ≈2 cm long          Flowers - tiny

67

# Red Mangrove

*Rhizophora mangle*
Family: Rhizophoraceae

Native Tree

**Found in Blue Hole Park and Walsingham Nature Reserve**

Germinating seed ready to fall
and float

Red mangrove prop roots seen at low tide

This salt-loving plant borders calm bays, salt ponds and lagoons. It gets its name from its interior red wood. It is an excellent natural protector of coastlines as its dense root system holds down the muddy substrate and buffers the coast from strong wave action. Unique to this mangal are its prop roots, which grow down from the trunk and branches entering the water from the air above, forming a dense biomass along the shoreline. The trunk is gray or grayish-brown, ridged and uneven. Leaves are a deep-green, leathery texture, and elliptical in shape. They form opposite each other on the stems and have smooth margins. Flowers are pale yellow, have four petals and produce one big seed that germinates while still attached to the tree. A long (up to 2.5 cm) leathery radicle (embryo that becomes the root) grows from the seed and helps this seed survive its fall into shallow water, floating to a new location. Flowers form in summer and autumn. This flowering plant survives in salt water by excreting salt through its leaves and also filtering it out before it enters the roots. The wood is hard and tight-grained with a reddish-brown color.

Height - 10 m or more                    Leaf - 5-15 cm long                    Flower - 1-2 cm across

# Black Mangrove

*Avicennia nitida*
Family: Avicenniaceae

Native Tree

**Found in Blue Hole Park and Walsingham Nature Reserve**

Black mangrove is an evergreen tree forming the next line of coastal defense, inland from the red mangrove. A striking feature of this tree that distinguishes it from the red mangrove are the many roots that shoot upward from the water (called pneumatophores), enabling the tree to have more surface area for gas exchange. The bark is dark-gray or brown and smooth. Leaves are dark-green, leathery and oblong. They are opposite and have smooth margins. They are capable of excreting salt; look closely for evidence of this right on the surface of the leaf. Flowers are creamy- white with 4 petals and are produced from spring to fall. The flower turns into an oblong fruit that has one pointed end. It is berry-like and dark-green and 2.5-5 cm long.

Height - to 10 m                  Leaf - 2.75-9 cm long                  Flower - 5-8 mm petals

69

# French Tamarisk

*Tamarix gallica*
Family: Tamaricaceae

Naturalized Tree

**Found in Cooper's Island Nature Reserve and North Shore Railway Trail**

Locally known as spruce, this introduced evergreen shrub or tree was planted as a dense windbreak on parts of the North Shore. Its origin is the Mediterranean region. Like some native trees, it has the ability to excrete salt through its leaves. The plant has numerous branches and its shape can take many forms, with the branches often arching toward the ground. Sometimes it is more upright like a tree, other times it looks more like a dense shrub. Its bark is gray, smooth when young, then developing splits as it matures. Its needle-like leaves are scale-like, clasping and alternate. Pink flowers are produced in spring and early summer and are in the form of long sprays of dense spikes.

Height - to 10 m                    Leaf - 1 mm or less                    Flower spikes - ≈10 cm long

70

# Saltmarsh Ox-Eye

*Borrichia frutescens*
Family: Compositae

Native Shrub

**Found in Walsingham Nature Reserve**

Isolated stands of this plant are found in the eastern part of Bermuda, especially Walsingham, near salt marshes and salt water lagoons. A good-sized stand exists in Walsingham Reserve. It is a shrub that is more upright than branching, bearing thick, grayish-green leaves. It is taller and more upright than its relative, the sea ox-eye. Young stems have gray hairs while older stems are woody. Leaves are opposite and shaped as elongated ovals. There is often a small point at the end of the leaf. Some leaves have smooth margins, others have symmetric indentations along the sides near their point of attachment to the stem. Flowers are yellow with 12-30 rays (petals). Flowers are solitary or few and are produced in summer and autumn.

Height - 0.3-1.3 m                    Leaf - 2.5-7.5 cm long                    Flower - 2.5 cm broad

# Bermuda Palmetto

*Sabal bermudana*
Family: Palmae

Endemic Tree

**Found on all walks**

Above: unripe seeds, below: ripe seeds

This endemic tree used to be second to the Bermuda cedar in dominance. It is common in upland coastal habitats. The plant has a fan-shaped palm with yellow markings on leaf blade margins and a spine tapering from the petiole to the middle of each palm. The petiole which connects the palm leaf to the trunk is smooth, which distinguishes it from the Chinese fan palm whose petiole is jagged bearing sharp spines. Small whitish flowers are produced in spikes in the spring and summer. The palmetto bears oval, blackish fruits, that are green when young. An intoxicating beverage called "Bibey" was produced from the fruit by early colonists, however this was halted when the palmetto population was seen to be shrinking.[5,19,21] Tan fibers hang from the leaf blades. These are used by the endemic white-eyed vireo to weave their cup-shaped nest.[28] The trunk is tan and has circular and vertical grooves, averaging 250 cm in diameter.

Height - 10 m to 15 m          Leaf - greater than 1.5 m across          Flower - tiny          Fruits (drupes) - 1.5-2.2 cm

# Chinese Fan Palm

*Livistonia chinensis*
Family: Palmae

Naturalized Tree

**Found near Whalebone Bay, Cooper's Island Nature Reserve, North Shore Railway Trail**

Above and left: note spines on petiole

Sometimes confused with the Bermuda palmetto, this introduced palm is invading the habitat of the endemic palmetto. This palm frond is also fan-shaped but leaf blades lack a spine running from the petiole to the middle of the palm. The structure (petiole) that connects the leaf blade or frond to the trunk has sharp spines that distinguish it from the Bermuda palmetto whose petiole is smooth. The leaves are broad and cut away into narrow segments and their tips hang down beneath the palm, almost drooping. Flowers are produced in clusters in spring and summer, and are tiny and white. Oval fruits are bright-turquoise (blue-green) when mature. The trunk is grayish-brown and shows leaf scars.

Height - to 10-15 m                 Leaf - greater than 1.5 m across                 Flower - tiny

73

# Natal Plum

*Carissa grandiflora*
Family: Apocynaceae

Naturalized Shrub

**Found near Whalebone Bay and Rail Trail**

This tall and dense shrub is found on rocky hillsides and is planted as a hedge in some gardens.  The leaves are a shiny, dark-green, and have a tough leathery appearance which helps them withstand salt spray.  The leaves are opposite and between some of them emanates a two-pronged sharp spine, 2-5 cm in length, capable of puncturing skin.  The plant produces a fragrant five-petaled white flower that evolves into a natal plum. The plum is red and contains black seeds when ripe.  It is edible despite the sticky, white sap it contains.  Jams are produced from this fruit.

Height to 5 m                                Leaf - 2.5-7.5 cm                                Flower - 5 cm diameter

# Forestiera

*Forestiera segregata*
Family: Oleaceae

Native Tree

Found in Walsingham Nature Reserve, Nonsuch Island

This evergreen shrub or tree has smooth light-gray bark. There are usually multiple trunks at its base. Oval leaves are produced opposite each other with smooth margins that look like deep-green leather. They are slightly pointed. The flowers are found in small clusters, greenish-yellow in color, and form in the axils of last year's leaves. Flowers are produced in autumn and winter, as leaves fall in November. The fruit is a dark purple to black oval ranging from 5-11 mm long. Its habitat is coastal uplands, though it is losing its habitat to invasive species that out-compete it for space thus its population is dwindling.

Height - to 7 m          Leaf - 2-7 cm long; 1-1.9 cm wide          Flower - small

# Fiddlewood

*Citharexylum spinosum*
Family: Verbenaceae

Naturalized Tree

**Found in Cooper's Island Nature Reserve**

Fiddlewood is found in coastal uplands and near mangrove areas. It was introduced from the West Indies and is considered invasive. N.L. Britton wrote in 1918 that it was "common on hillsides, especially in Hamilton Parish....recorded as introduced about 1830. Useful only for firewood and shade. A tree of rapid growth, the wood is light in weight."[5] The fiddlewood is characterized by large elliptical or oblong-elliptical leaves. The petiole that connects the leaf to a branch is a distinctive orange. The leaves turn a golden-orange in spring or early summer, then drop their leaves, which are replaced by new green leaves and trains of small white, fragrant flowers. Flowers are produced in summer and autumn. The trunk is light-brown and appears papery. It can reach almost one meter in diameter. The fruit (drupe) is oblong and shiny, first red, then turning black. It is about 1 cm long and is produced in bunches (like grapes).

Height - 16+ m                    Leaf - to 20 cm long                    Flower (clusters or racemes) - 10-20 cm

# Allspice

*Pimenta dioica*
Family: Myrtaceae

Naturalized Tree

**Found in Blue Hole Park, Walsingham Nature Reserve, Alfred Blackburn Smith Audubon Reserve**

This tree produces large, stiff, green, oblong leaves. The leaves form opposite each other. Small white clusters of flowers give way to greenish, berries that ultimately become reddish-black. Flowers are small and white and form in clusters. Flowers are produced in summer and autumn. Both its leaves and flowers are fragrant smelling. The berries produced by this tree are used in cooking, known to many as allspice. Allspice is not a mix of all spices, but the dried, unripe berry produced by this plant. The trunk is pale silver-brown and is sometimes peeling. The wood produced by this tree is quite dense. The fragrance created by the allspice oils and dense wood may be adaptations that better enable it to survive in insect rich environments.[32] It can be found in coastal uplands/hillsides.

Height - to 10 m                    Leaf - 7.5-15 cm long                    Flower - small

# Surinam Cherry

*Eugenia uniflora*
Family: Myrtaceae

Naturalized Shrub/Tree

**Found in Blue Hole Park, Walsingham Nature Reserve, Whalebone Bay**

This tree is often seen in coastal upland areas as well as near marshes. Shiny green leaves form oppositely on the branches of the Surinam cherry. The leaves are stiff, oval and come to a point at the end. They are shiny above and paler underneath. New leaves are a shiny reddish color. The trunk is a silver-tan color, smooth, though peeling in some areas. The flowers are creamy-white, bearing 4 petals, found singly or in groups of up to 4 and are seen in summer and autumn. They are produced in long stalks in the leaf axils. The Surinam cherry is considered an invasive species as they have taken over habitats of native and endemic trees. Birds have dispersed their seeds (fruits twice a year) throughout the island, since the tree was introduced in the 1800's. Its fragrant flowers produce bright-red cherries that are used locally in jams and cooking. Fruits look like mini-pumpkins, bearing furrows from top to bottom.

Height - 5 m          Leaf - 2.5-6 cm long          Flower - tiny          Fruit - ≈1-2 cm diameter

# White Stopper

*Eugenia monticola*
Family: Myrtaceae

Native Tree

**Found in Walsingham Nature Reserve, Cooper's Island Nature Reserve**

Above and right: White Stopper with common leaf minor infestation

This native evergreen tree is found in coastal uplands. Leaves are oblong or elliptical with a rounded and smooth margin. The leaves are usually mottled with yellow on their surface due to leaf minor infestation, though this does not seem to reduce the tree's viability.[27] The tree has a straight trunk and stands upright. The bark is smooth and a mottled gray-tan. The mature tree silhouette has a tufted appearance on top. The name "white stopper" may have come from the fact that the berry it produces stops diarrhea. Flowers are produced in clusters (racemes) and each flower has four petals. The tree flowers in the autumn. The fruit is about 1 cm in diameter and smooth black. Lefroy said that it had "hard to find flowers or berries".[17]

Height - to 7 m                    Leaf - 2-7 cm long                    Flower - tiny

# Bermuda Bean

*Phaseolus lignosus*
Family: Leguminosae

Endemic Vine

**Found in Walsingham Nature Reserve**

This rare beauty is a challenge to find. It is a perennial herb with thin, woody stems found in rocky woodlands near coastlines. It produces a sprawling vine. Its leaflets are rounded at the base and come to a point at their apex. Leaves are found in groups of three. Flowers are produced in clusters at the end of a stem or branch and range from white to purple, but sometimes are pale-yellow. Flowers are produced primarily in summer and autumn however if the plant is in a sheltered location it may produce flowers at other times of the year.

Height - Stem to 7 m long        Leaf- to 10 cm long        Flower - 7.5-12.5 cm long cluster (raceme)        Pod - ≈7.5 cm long

80

# Jumbie Bean or Wild Mimosa

*Leucaena leucocephala*
Family: Leguminosae

Naturalized Shrub

Found near Whalebone Bay, Blue Hole Park,
Warwick Long Bay, Spittal Pond Nature
Reserve, Fort Scaur Railway Trail

This evergreen perennial shrub/tree has alternate leaves that are pinnate (look like ferns). Leaves are made up of small leaflets that are 0.5-1.5 cm long. Considered by many an invasive pest or weed, it is frequently seen on the way to a beach. Older plants become quite tall and woody. Flowers are yellow to creamy-white, round ball-like structures produced throughout the year with stamen standing tall inside the flower, about three to five times the size of a petal. A long pod (first green, then brown) is produced containing seeds.

Height - to 12+ m          Leaf - 10-30 cm long w/6-20 pinnae          Flower - ≈4 cm diameter          Pod - 10-15 cm long

# Brazil or Mexican Pepper Tree

*Schinus terebinthifolia*
Family: Anacardiaceae

Naturalized Tree

**Found in Blue Hole Reserve, Cooper's Island Nature Reserve,
Walsingham Nature Reserve, Fort Scaur Railway Trail**

Brazil pepper
berries in January

Originating from Brazil, this extremely invasive tree is found on upland hillsides and many other locales in Bermuda. It is salt tolerant. The evergreen leaves are pinnate (comprised of small leaflets off a common stem) with 3-9 leaflets oppositely placed. The leaflets are elliptical in shape and have small undulations along the margins. Flower petals are tiny and greenish-white in color, produced in a cluster. The stamen of the flowers are yellow. Bright-red berries form, only on the female tree (the male tree produces no berries) and are often used as Christmas decorations if humans reach them before the birds disperse the seeds. It has been declared a noxious weed in many parts of the world.

Height - to 8 m, spread -3 m        Leaflets - to 7 cm long, 1-2.5 cm wide        Flower cluster - 5-11 cm long, petals 2 mm long

# Hibiscus

*Hibiscus rosa sinensis*
Family: Malvaceae

Naturalized Shrub

**Found enroute to Blue Hole Park, Walsingham Nature Reserve, and Warwick Long Bay**

The brilliant eye-catching flowers on the hibiscus suggest why this shrub was introduced. This native of China forms a dense, attractive hedge to separate property. Flowers range from red to pinks, yellow and white, and occasionally a mixture of two colors. Green leaves are oval but more rounded at their base and come to a point at the apex of the leaf. Their edges have small teeth. It is generally not found right near a beach, but often seen on the way there! It has been said that if trimmed down, new flowers appear the next day. Most flowers do bloom for just one day. Some plants flower throughout the entire year though most bloom primarily in spring and summer. This is a truly beautiful tropical (and ornamental) plant.

Height - 4-5 m                    Leaf - 7.5-20 cm long                    Flower - 10-15 cm long

# Jamaica Vervain

*Valerianoides jamaicenti*
Family: Verbenaceae

Native Herb

**Found in Cooper's Island Nature Reserve and South Shore Park**

This herb is found in fields and waste places often near coastlines. Leaves are sometimes alternate though more often opposite and have an oblong or oval shape. The margins have coarse serrations and narrow at their base. Large central veins within the leaves may appear reddish. A spike arising from the top of the stem looks like a thin green spear, which then produces delicate purplish-blue flowers projecting from its sides. The flowers have 5 petals and usually form somewhere from the middle to the bottom of the spike. The spike can range from 15-40 cm tall. Flowers are produced from spring to autumn.

Height - 0.3-1.2 m                    Leaf - 1.2-9 cm long                    Flower - 0.8 cm across

# Cape Weed

*Phyla nodiflora*
Family: Verbenaceae

Native Ground Cover

**Found near Spittal Pond Nature Reserve, Whalebone Bay, Cooper's Island Nature Reserve, and Blue Hole Park**

Found just inland of dunes, rocky shores and mangroves, where soil exists, this hearty (very abundant) weed is nicknamed Frog Fruits.[21] It forms a ground cover consisting of reddish trailing stems bearing green leaves. The leaves are thick, oval but wider in the area furthest from the stem (spatulate). Jagged teeth can be seen on the outer edges of the leaf blade. The leaves are green with reddish edges. They are opposite with sometimes four leaves arising from the same position on the stem. A wiry stem holds tiny pinkish flowers. Flowers are pale-pink clusters produced from spring to autumn.

Height - 0.33-1 m                    Leaf - to 5 cm long                    Flower - 1.3-2.5 cm long

# Seven-Year Apple

*Casasia clusiifolia*
Family: Rubiaceae

Native Shrub

**Found on Nonsuch Island and private gardens**

Left: D. Wingate examines
a healthy Seven-Year Apple
Upper right: Flower
Lower right: Fruit and
heart-shaped leaves

This branching, woody shrub has leaves that are clustered, shiny and leathery appearing waxed. Their shape is oval but more rounded at the apex. They look heart-shaped due to a notch at the tip of the leaf. Small trumpet-like flowers form in clusters at the terminal end of branches. Flowers are usually produced in spring or early summer and are a creamy, yellowish-white. Occasionally flowers have been observed into the autumn. The fruit is the size and shape of a lime. It lives on coastal hillsides and a stand exists in Tucker Town and on Nonsuch. This plant is extremely rare and endangered.

Height - 1-3 m          Leaf - 5-15 cm long          Flower - ≈4 cm long, 2 cm across          Fruit - 5-7 cm long

# Small Passion Flower or Inkberry

*Passiflora suberosa*
Family: Passifloraceae

Native Herb

**Found on Nonsuch Island and private gardens**

Above: Small passion flower tendrils

This delicate plant grows as a vine along rock walls and in shady coastal areas, as well as inland in the understory of native forests. It is inconspicuous when not flowering, so easily missed. The leaves are round-oval shape and often there is a slight point at the apex (outer tip) of the leaf. Their color is dark-green and their margins (edges) are smooth. The runners or stems look like green wires and have tendrils that allow the plant to secure itself as it spreads. Older stems may appear woody. Its tiny green flower (approximately a centimeter across) is often produced in pairs. The flower is a host of the Gulf Fritillary Butterfly's caterpillar and are produced in summer and autumn.[27] A deep-purple (almost black) oval berry is produced.

Height - 0.75-2 m long          Leaf - 3.5-5 cm long, 2+ cm wide          Flower - tiny

# Japanese Pittosporum

*Pittosporum tobira*
Family: Pittosporaceae

Naturalized Tree

**Found in Cooper's Island Nature Reserve and Warwick Long Bay**

Pittosporum is an introduced tree with elegant natural design. Its shape can take on a bonsai-style form. Originating from the Far East, it may have inspired bonsai artists there. The leaves are thick, have smooth margins, and are dark-green. Their upper surface has a waxy appearance while the leaf has a stiff, leathery feel. Leaf shape is oval with a blunt end. The leaves grow in whorls around the stems and branches. At the center of the whorls, clusters of fragrant white flowers are produced in the spring. The flowers become a cluster of green fruit, which turns to a grainy-brown and holds bright-red seeds. The trees can be seen at the above locations and on many residential properties.

Height - to 4 m          Leaf - 5-9 cm long          Fruit - 2-3 cm long          Flower - 1.3 cm long

# Jamaica Dogwood

*Dodonaea viscosa*  Britton: *Dodonaea jamaicensis*
Family: Sapindaceae

Native Shrub

**Found in Cooper's Island Nature Reserve and Alfred Blackburn Smith Audubon Reserve**

Papery winged fruit bearing seeds

Jamaica Dogwood is found in sandy soils near coastlines and upland habitats. It is a large woody evergreen shrub. Its leaves are oblong but elongated, making it easy to distinguish from other shrubs. The leaves have smooth margins and a tapered base. The shrub produces clusters of small, yellow-green flowers that bloom in spring and summer. These turn into a dark-tan, papery winged fruit that contains black seeds. This fruit is about 1.2 cm long. Its species name, viscosa, means sticky or viscous, referring to a sticky coating on both surfaces of the leaves.

Height - to 6+ m, to 3 m wide          Leaf - 5-10 cm long, 1.5 cm wide          Flowers - ≈1 cm across, cluster - 3-8 cm diameter

# Bermuda Snowberry

*Chiococca bermudiana*
Family: Rubiaceae

Endemic Shrub

**Found in Walsingham Nature Reserve, Nonsuch Island, Alfred Blackburn Smith Audubon Reserve, Botanical Gardens**

This beautiful endemic shrub is found on coastal hillsides or forest areas. It is not easy to find as it is often out-competed by invasive species. Lefroy, in the late 1800's observed that both the fruit and flower were fragrant and it was common.[17] Less competition for space existed then. It is a sprawling shrub, with shiny tough leaves that are oval in shape, forming a point at their tip. The flowers are produced in the fall, and sometimes early in the year. They are fragrant, yellow, shaped like tiny bells, and form on opposite sides of a common stem (peduncle). These then turn into attractive white berries, which are pleasing to view and appealing to birds.

Height - to 2 m, to 5 m wide             Leaf - 8-10 cm long             Flower - 0.5 cm diameter

# Box Briar

Native Shrub

**Found on Nonsuch Island**

*Randia aculeate*
Family: Rubiaceae

Box Briar is a rare evergreen shrub found in coastal uplands. The leaves are small and tightly clustered on the stem. They are bright-green, leathery and have smooth margins, and are oval yet broad across their middle. The plant has sharp thorns that arise in pairs at a v-shaped angle along the stem. White flowers are produced in summer and autumn. Green berries turn whitish when mature. It is found in small areas of Warwick and Paget Parishes.

Height - 1-3 m tall                    Leaf - 1-2 cm long                    Flower - 1 cm across, 0.5 cm long

# Darrell's Fleabane

*Erigeron darrellianus*
Family: Compositae

Endemic Herb

**Found on Nonsuch Island and Alfred Blackburn Smith Audubon Reserve**

Dried flowers from Darrell's Fleabane

This endemic herb is deep-green with elongated oval-shaped leaves. The leaves are almost spear-shaped and have tiny, barely visible serrations along their edges. The leaves form around their stem in whorls and the plant appears quite dense. Tall stems bearing clusters of tiny, white daisy-like flowers are seen in spring through autumn. The flowers have a yellow center. Flowers dry and release their seeds.

Height - ≈1.2 m tall          Leaves - 8 cm long, 1.5 cm at widest point          Flower - ≈1 cm diameter

92

# Turnera

*Turnera ulminifolia*
Family: Turneraceae

Native Herb

Found on Ferry Reach Rd., on the right when heading to Whalebone Bay and under cultivation at Fort Scaur

This attractive native is a standout on coastal hillsides and roadsides, though it is somewhat rare. It is an herb with lanceolate (shaped like a lance, narrowing at the tip) or oval-shaped leaves that have jagged (serrated) edges. Leaves are a dark-green and come to a point. They usually form a whorl with several leaves arising at the same position around the stem. Sometimes leaves alternate. Bright-yellow flowers have five petals and are produced in summer and autumn. Small yellowish-green round capsules contain numerous tiny seeds.

Height - 0.30-1+ m                   Leaf - 3.5-8 cm long                   Flower - ≈5 cm diameter

# Yellow Wood or West Indian Satinwood

*Zanthoxylum flavum*
Family: Rutaceae

Native Tree

**Found on Nonsuch Island and Stokes Reserve**

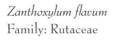

This native tree is rarely seen in Bermuda.  It is endangered due to cutting and being out-competed by other plants.  A small tree can be found in Stokes Reserve in St. George's Parish.  Nonsuch also hosts some Yellow Wood.  Historical records show it was wide spread but sought after for its valuable lumber.  Government orders as early as 1632 limit its exportation to England due to over cutting.[5]  The tree has alternate pinnate leaves (the leaves are actually leaflets, which form opposite each other, 5-11 leaflets along one big leaf) and is evergreen.  Its bark is smooth and different shades of gray. Leaves and twigs have tiny hairs on them when the plant is young.  Leaf blades are oblong or oval and may be smooth or slightly scalloped on their margins.  Their upper surface is shiny.  Flowers are produced in terminal clusters, are yellow and produce a strong scent that is very attractive to bees.  Flowers are seen erratically at any time of the year with different trees on different schedules for flower production.[27]  They produce a tiny black seed.

Height - to 10-12 m          Leaf - 10-30 cm long, terminal leaf smaller          Flower - tiny          Cluster of flowers - 7-14 cm long

# Brier Bush or Grey Nickers

*Caesalpina bonduc*
Synonyms: *Guilandina crista, Guilandina bonduc*
Family: Leguminosae

Native Shrub

**Found on Nonsuch Island and under cultivation at Horseshoe Bay entrance**

Above: curved thorns & prickles on stems

Very rare, perhaps because homeowners find it difficult to manage due to its large size and challenging thorns, Brier Bush is considered endangered. The vine has curved thorns on both the stem and at the base of every leaf. The leaves are actually leaflets, which form opposite each other, usually fourteen leaflets along one big leaf. The shape of each leaflet is oblong, some with a small point at the end. They are bright-green and have smooth margins. It produces beautiful pale-yellow flowers in clusters that develop into brownish oval seed pods. The flowers are produced year-round. Britton wrote "its seeds presumably brought to Bermuda through the ocean, as it is an abundant coastal species in the Bahamas." [5] In Bermuda it tends to grow in rocky upland regions and is not a dominant coastal shrub. It is well worth knowing and cultivating!

Height - to 6 m          Leaf - 30 cm-60 cm          Leaflets - 3.5-8.5 cm long          Flower (raceme) - 10-37 cm

# Southern Hackberry

*Celtis laevigata*
Family: Ulmacea

Native Tree

**Found in Walsingham Nature Reserve**

Trunk of Southern Hackberry

This tree can be seen on rocky hillsides and woods. It differs from other similar looking trees in that it has alternating leaves. The leaves are oval to lanceolate (shaped like a lance, narrowing at the tip), coming to a point at the tip. They can often be quite round near their base, almost heart shaped. The leaves usually have smooth margins (edges). They fall in the autumn, being replaced in the spring. The tree produces tiny clusters of white flowers at leaf axils in the spring. The trunk is a mottled light-brown to grey, sometimes greenish due to moss or lichen growth. Tiny berries (fruit) ripen in the fall. The green unripe berry matures to an orange-brown color.

Height - to 14 m                     Leaf - 6-8 cm long, 3-4 cm wide                     Flower - tiny

# GLOSSARY

**Axil**: space between two adjacent plant parts; ex. area between stem and leaf

**Axillar**: forming in the axils of the plant

**Compound leaf**: leaf blade is divided into several leaflets or sections

**Corolla**: all of the petals of a flower

**Crenate**: showing a scalloped margin

**Dentate**: leaf margin with teeth projecting out at a right angle to the leaf margin

**Drupe**: fruit that produces a stony inner core, usually with one seed

**Endemic species**: organism found only in one area of the world; genetically unique

**Entire margins**: leaf edge that is smooth, with no indentations

**Halophyte**: a salt-tolerant terrestrial plant

**Herb**: a non-woody plant

**Introduced species**: organism living in an area because humans relocated it there or humans unintentionally relocated it there

**Lanceolate**: leaf shape 4 times as long as broad, in the shape of a lance which narrows at end

**Leaf apex**: the outer tip of a leaf, furthest from petiole

**Margin**: edge of a leaf

**Native species**: organism living in an area that arrived there by natural means

**Naturalized species**: an introduced (by man) species that can reproduce and survive in its new location

**Node**: a joint (slightly narrow region) in a stem, bearing a leaf or leaves

**Peduncle**: the stalk of a cluster of flowers

**Petiole**: slender stem connecting leaf to plant

**Pinnate**: leaf blades are arranged on both sides of a midrib of a leaf or an axis

**Pubescent**: covered with fine soft hairs

**Raceme**: upright single stalk bearing tiny single flowers; lower flowers usually bloom first

**Shrub**: a woody plant not having a main trunk, usually smaller than a tree

**Simple leaf**: leaf blade is one segment

**Sinuate leaved**: leaves have wavy margins

**Stamen**: pollen producing part of a flower (male), usually more than one and in the central region of flower

**Tree**: a woody plant with a main trunk, usually larger than a shrub

**Oblanceolate**: Similar shape to lanceolate but petiole attaches to the narrower end of the leaf, while wider, rounder end is furthest from the plant

**Umbel**: a cluster of flowers that is flat topped and looks like an upside down umbrella

**Whorled**: three or more structures (ex. leaves) that form a circle around a stem; all at the same node

Compound leaf showing pinnate, opposite leaflets
Grey Nickers (*Caesalpina bonduc*)

# REFERENCES

1.    Benson L.  Plant Classification. Lexington (MA): DC Heath and Company; 1959
2.    Bermuda Biodiversity Project. [Internet] Bermuda: Bermuda Aquarium, Museum & Zoo; 2002 (cited 2007 October 7) Available from: www.bamz.org/biodiversity/cahow.htm
3.    Bermuda Zoological Society.  Guide to Nonsuch Island "Living Museum" Nature Reserve. Bermuda: Bermuda Zoological Society; April 2001
4.    Bermuda Zoological Society. The Sandy Shore, Project Nature Field Study Guides. Bermuda: Bermuda Zoological Society; 1994
5.    Britton NL.  Flora of Bermuda. New York (NY): Scribner and Sons; 1918
6.    Cavaliere AR, Barnes RD, Cook CB. Field Guide to the Conspicuous Flora and Fauna of Bermuda.  Bermuda: Bermuda Biological Station for Research Special Publication No. 31; 1992
7.    Council of Science Editors, Style Manual Committee.  Scientific style and format: the CSE manual for authors, editors, and publishers. 7th ed. Reston (VA): The Council; 2006
8.    Cox DD.  A Naturalist's Guide to Seashore Plants; An Ecology for Eastern North America. Syracuse (NY): Syracuse University Press; 2003
9.    Davidson C.  Hiking Bermuda, 20 Nature Walks & Day Hikes. VegaNet Publications; 2006
10.   Doe, Fiona.  Personal communication
11.   Duncan WH and Duncan MB.  The Smithsonian Guide to Seaside Plants of the Gulf and Atlantic Coasts. Washington (DC): Smithsonian Press; 1987
12.   Duncan WH and Duncan MB.  Wildflowers of the Eastern United States. Athens (GA): University of Georgia Press; 1999
13.   Gilman, Edward. *Wedelia trilobata*, Florida Cooperative Extension Service; 1999
14.   Greene L.  Bermuda Museum of Natural History, Collection's Officer, Personal communication
15.   Greene L.  Gardener's World or Green Thumb Column. Bermuda: *Mid-Ocean News*; May 1999-September 2007
16.   Horsfield R.  cartographer.  The Bermuda Islands. Warwick (BDA): Island Maps; 1996
17.   Lefroy JH.  Contributions to the Natural History of The Bermudas, Volume 1, Part II Botany. Washington (DC): Government Printing Office; 1884 Edited by Jones JM and Goode GB
18.   Phillips-Watlington C.  Bermuda's Botanical Wonderland a Field Guide. London (GB): Macmillan Education Ltd; 1996
19.   Rueger BF and von Wallmenich TN.  Human impact on the forests of Bermuda: the decline of endemic cedar and palmetto since 1609, recorded in the Holocene pollen record of Devonshire Marsh.  Journal of Plaeolimnology 16: 59-66; 1996
20.   Silberhorn GM. Common Plants of the Mid-Atlantic Coast, A Field Guide. Baltimore (MD): The Johns Hopkins UniversityPress;1999
21.   Sterrer W and Cavaliere AR.  Bermuda's Seashore Plants and Seaweeds. Flatts (BDA): Bermuda Zoological Society; 1998

22. Sterrer W. Marine Fauna and Flora of Bermuda. New York (NY): Wiley-Interscience; 1986 Edition

23. Thieret JM. Revising Author, Niering WA. Original Author. National Audubon Society Field Guide to Northern American Wildflowers; Eastern Region. Alfred A. Knopf, Inc. Chanticleer Press, Inc.; 2001

24. Thomas ML. Marine and Oceanic Island Ecology of Bermuda. Bermuda: Bermuda Aquarium, Natural History Museum and Zoo; 2001

25. Thomas ML. The Natural History of Bermuda. Flatts (BDA): Bermuda Zoological Society; 2004

26. Ward J. Bermuda Director of Conservation Services. Personal communication

27. Wingate DB. Personal communication

28. Wingate H. Personal communication

## INTERNET RESOURCES

29. http://plants.ifas.ufl.edu/ juncus.html
30. http://plants.ifas.ufl.edu/ pasvag.html
31. http://www.audubon.bm
32. http://backyardnature.net/yucatan/allspice.htm
33. http://www.Bermudaonline.org/flora.html
34. http://www.calflora.net/floraofbermuda/plantlist.html
35. http://www. cals.arizona.edu
36. http://www.conifers.org/cu/ju/bermudiana.htm
37. http://www.eoearth.org/article/Bermuda_subtropical_conifer_forests
38. http://www.hort.purdue.edu/newcrop/morton/surinam_cherry.html
39. http://www.mhhe.com/biosci/pae/botany/botany_map/articles/article_23.html
40. http://www.museum.state.il.us/exhibits/ice_ages/when/ice/ages.html
41. http://plants.nrcs.usda.gov
42. http://www.plantatlas.usf.edu
43. http://www.plants.usda.gov
44. http://www.sciweb.nybg.org
45. http://www.sfrc.ufl.edu/4h/Red_mangrove/redmangr.htm
46. http://www.tva.gov/river/landandshore
47. http://www.weather.bm
48. http://www.weatherunderground.com

# INDEX

AJP                                                                                      AJP

## About the Author

Amy K. Pearson, an American, has taught science for 30 years as a faculty member of the Bancroft School, an independant day school in Worcester, Massachusetts. Since 1997, she has traveled to Bermuda annually to study, teach and learn about island ecology. She has worked with groups of teachers but more often high school students, introducing them to the unique ecology of an oceanic island. She was chosen to be a 2007 National Oceanographic and Atmospheric Association (NOAA) Teacher at Sea, spending seventeen days on a NOAA research vessel. She has also received the Bancroft School Carpe Diem Award for excellence in teaching. She has a Bachelor of Arts degree in Biology from Clark University in Worcester, MA. Her love of plants and the ocean inspired her to write this book. Observing the delicate balance of coastal plants, especially on a tiny, isolated island, stimulated her desire to show others their beauty and importance in nature.

Printed in China